EQUALITIES AND APPROXIMATIONS

with fortran programming

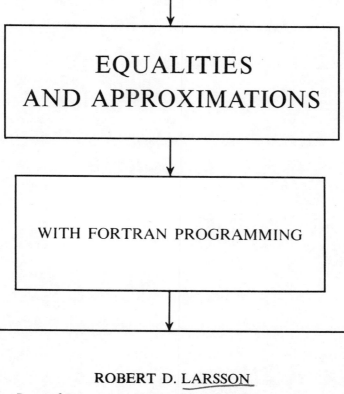

EQUALITIES
AND APPROXIMATIONS

WITH FORTRAN PROGRAMMING

ROBERT D. LARSSON

Dean of Instruction, Mohawk Valley Community College

JOHN WILEY & SONS, INC.

NEW YORK · LONDON · SYDNEY

Copyright © 1963 by John Wiley & Sons, Inc.

Library of Congress Catalog Card Number: 63-20634

Printed in the United States of Am

dedicated to Winslow S. Parkhurst

PREFACE

This textbook is designed for an enrichment course in mathematics and contains material not regularly given in a secondary-school course or in any traditional first-year course in college.

It is hoped that a course based on this textbook would give a student a broader foundation in mathematics and better prepare him for the calculus; a course in trigonometry would be a necessary prerequisite.

A unique feature is the option of integrating Fortran programming for an electronic computer into the complete course for all the types of problems considered. The book is self-contained and requires no prior knowledge of programming or computers.

However, all of the work on Fortran may be omitted without affecting the continuity of the material in any way.

The material in this textbook has been given by the author in an enrichment program for high-school students since 1961. It also was the basis of a course given in National Science Foundation Summer Institutes for High Ability Secondary-School Students in 1962 and 1963. It may be taught in one or two semesters, depending upon the depth of coverage undertaken, especially in the use of the computer.

I would like to acknowledge the support given me by the National Science Foundation under whose grant NSF-G21180, in the Cooperative College-School Science Program, the original lecture notes were prepared which formed the basis of my book.

I express my deep appreciation to Professor John M. Perry, Clarkson College of Technology, Professor Seymour Schuster, Carleton College, and Professor Roy Dubisch, University of Washington, for their many helpful comments and suggestions.

This book was written while I was professor of mathematics at Clarkson College of Technology.

Utica, New York   ROBERT D. LARSSON
July, 1963

CONTENTS

1 | GROUPS

1. Sets and Equations

The concept of a set is of great usefulness in mathematics.

Definition. A set is a collection of numbers, symbols, points, objects, etc., called elements, which have some distinguishing characteristics in common.

We speak of the set of even integers, the set of positive integers, the set of books on a shelf, the set of rational numbers, the set of people in a room, just to cite a few examples.

Now given two elements b and c belonging to a set S, one can ask whether there is an element x, belonging to the set S, such that

$$bx = c.$$

But immediately we have introduced another concept. What do we mean by the expression bx? Is it multiplication in the ordinary sense of the word? If so, then the elements in the set S under consideration must be such that they can be combined by ordinary multiplication.

For example, if our set S was composed of the men in a room, we could not combine one man with another man and obtain a third man. But if our set S was the set of committees made up from men in a room, and b and c each represented a committee, then it might be possible to combine committee b with some other committee x and obtain a committee identical to committee c. However, it also might be impossible.

Thus we see that in any equation one must define not only the set S whose elements appear in the various expressions in the equation, but the operation or operations by which the elements may be combined as well.

1

We can illustrate this in the following examples:

Given the set S of odd integers and the operation of multiplication, does the equation

$$3x = 15$$

have a solution? In other words, is there an element called x belonging to the set of odd integers, such that the left-hand side of the equation could replace the right-hand side? The answer is obviously yes, since the element x can be selected as the element 5, and 5 is an odd integer.

But suppose that we are given the set of odd integers and the operation of addition, does the equation

$$3 + x = 15$$

have a solution? The answer is no. There is no odd integer, x, which can be added to 3 to give 15. We all know that x would have to be 12, which is not an odd integer.

The linear equation in two variables is written as

$$ax + by = c.$$

If our set S is the set of integers and our operations are multiplication and addition, the linear equation

$$2x + 4y = 3$$

has no solution—where by a solution we mean values of x and y which belong to the set S. While, for example, it is true that $x = 1$ and $y = \frac{1}{4}$ satisfies the equation, $\frac{1}{4}$ is not a member of the set S. Can you see why no solution is possible in S? (Hint: $2x + 4y = 2(x + 2y)$.)

On the other hand, the equation

$$3x + 5y = 1$$

has an infinite number of solutions. It can be verified by direct substitution that

$$x = 2 + 5t$$

and

$$y = -1 - 3t$$

are solutions for all integral values of t.

There are many practical problems of this nature, since in production of various articles there can be no consideration given to part of an article, such as half of a book or a third of a car.

Consider the general quadratic equation

$$ax^2 + bx + c = 0,$$

where a, b, c are defined as coefficients and must all be members of the same set S. Our question is whether or not there is an element x belonging to S which satisfies the equation under the operations as defined.

If we select S as the set of integers and the operations as ordinary addition and multiplication, we can consider the following examples.

$$x^2 + 2x + (-3) = 0.$$

This has two solutions, $x = -3$ and $x = 1$, which are both members of the set S. ·

But the equation

$$2x^2 + 5x + 2 = 0$$

has only one solution, $x = -2$, belonging to the set of integers. The other, $x = -\frac{1}{2}$, does not. However, if we had taken S as the set of rational numbers, namely all those which can be expressed as the quotient of two integers, our quadratic would have two solutions belonging to the set S.

If we take S as the set of integers, the quadratic

$$x^2 + 2x + 5 = 0$$

has no solutions. If we take S as the set of all real numbers, it still has no solutions belonging to the set S. But if we extend S to include all complex numbers, those of the form $a + bi$, where a and b are real numbers, then the quadratic has two solutions. They are $-1 - 2i$ and $-1 + 2i$, where $i^2 = -1$.

It becomes evident that just because the coefficients in a given equation belong to some set S, the solutions need not belong to the same set S. The operations involved are part of the key as well.

Exercises

1. (a) Given the equation
$$2 + x = 12,$$
   find at least three sets of numbers to which the elements 2 and 12 belong and to which x belongs also.
   (b) Change the operation to multiplication and do the problem.
2. (a) Given the equation
$$3x = 5,$$
   find at least two sets of numbers to which the elements 3 and 5 belong and to which x does not belong.
   (b) Change the operation to addition and do the problem.
3. Give a set of numbers which contains three other sets of numbers. Define each subset carefully.
4. Given a set of ten men, form them into three committees A, B and C such that
$$A + B = C,$$
where $+$ means "combined with".

5. Given the linear equation
$$2x + 3y = 5,$$
find two solutions in the set of integers. Find two solutions in another set, to which 2, 3 and 5 also belong.

6. Why does the linear equation
$$2x + 4y = 3$$
have no solutions in the set of integers?

7. Form a quadratic equation whose coefficients belong to the set of integers, which has two distinct solutions in that set; no solutions in that set; only one solution in that set.

8. In problem 7, to what other sets do your solutions belong in each case? Do the coefficients belong to the same sets?

2. Properties of a Group

In order to develop a better foundation for the study of equations, we shall begin with the simplest example.

(1) $$b + x = c.$$

We shall ask what the sufficient conditions must be on a set S, containing b and c, in order that there shall exist a unique element x belonging to S and satisfying equation (1).

Now consider the set of even integers and some further properties of this set. If we add two even integers, such as 4 and 12, we obtain the even integer 16 as the sum. And the sum of 10 and 14 is 24, still another even integer. Although many examples may appear to verify some mathematical observation, such as the sum of two even integers is an even integer, one has no proof unless he has been able to exhaust all cases.

Since any even integer, by definition, is divisible by 2, we may write it in the form $2n$, where n is some integer. Then we have
$$2n + 2m = 2(n + m)$$
for the sum of two such even integers. But the sum of two integers is an integer, say p, and we obtain
$$2n + 2m = 2p.$$
This proves the assumption that the sum of any two even integers is an even integer. This leads us to an important definition.

Definition. A set of elements, with some prescribed operation by which any two of these elements may be combined, is said to be closed under that operation if the resulting combination is a member of the set.

Note that both the set and the operation must be prescribed. For example, the set of even integers is closed under multiplication also but not under division, since 2 divided by 2 is 1.

Note also that one counter example is enough to prove a statement false, while a thousand examples will not prove it true unless all the possibilities have been exhausted.

Other examples of closure which come to mind are the set of odd integers under multiplication, the set of all integers under addition, the set of positive rational numbers under division.

The even integer 0 has a special property under addition. For example, 0 plus 4 is 4, and 0 plus 30 is 30. In fact we see that

$$0 + 2n = 2n$$

for all n. Because of this property, the integer 0 is called the identity element under addition for the set of even integers.

We define the identity element as follows.

Definition. An element i belonging to the set is called the identity element if, under the operation, the combination of i with any other element b belonging to the set is the element b.

For the set of odd integers under multiplication, the number 1 is the identity element. Furthermore, it is evident that not all sets have an identity element under an operation. For example, consider the set of even integers under multiplication; 1 is not a member of the set.

To continue with the properties of the even integers, we note that with each even integer there is associated another even integer such that the sum under addition is the identity element. For example, 6 and -6 have a sum of 0. In general we show that

$$(-2n) + (2n) = 0$$

for all n. The element $-2n$ is called the inverse of the element $2n$. We make the following definition.

Definition. An element b^{-1} is called the inverse of an element b in the set if, under the operation, the combination of these two elements is the identity element.

Careful attention is directed here to the symbol b^{-1}. One should not think of the $^{-1}$ as being an exponent. The student is already familiar with other examples of this kind. In trigonometry we have

$$y = \sin x$$

and then, solving for x, we write

$$x = \text{arc sin } y$$

or
$$x = \sin^{-1} y,$$

where the $^{-1}$ is not an exponent, but denotes the inverse trigonometric function.

Unfortunately, we run out of convenient symbols many times and have to use duplicate ones. For example, the symbol (a, b) sometimes represents the coordinates of a point, sometimes the greatest common divisor of a and b and sometimes simply an ordered pair. One needs to be sure of the definition an author has made for such a symbol when he first used it.

Now we recall the associative law. If one is given three even integers, such as 2, 6 and 14 to add, it is evident that one can combine only two at a time. Then the sum of that pair is added to the remaining number. We have two ways of doing this:

$$(2 + 6) + 14 = 8 + 14 = 22$$

or

$$2 + (6 + 14) = 2 + 20 = 22.$$

We know that for all triples of integers this law, called the associative law, holds under both addition and multiplication. It does not hold under division, however, as observed in the following.

$$(2 \div 4) \div 14 = \tfrac{1}{2} \div 14 = \tfrac{1}{28}$$
$$2 \div (4 \div 14) = 2 \div \tfrac{2}{7} = 7$$

Note once again, and this point cannot be overemphasized, that most laws and properties hold under certain operations and not under others for a given set of elements. Not only must the set be defined but also the operation by which the elements are to be combined must be defined.

We define the associative law as follows.

Definition. Under addition, the associative law states that

$$(a + b) + c = a + (b + c)$$

and under multiplication, the associative law states that

$$(ab)c = a(bc).$$

We now define a group.

Definition. A set S of elements a, b, c, ... forms a group, under an operation, say $\oplus$, if:

1. The set S is closed under $\oplus$.
2. There is a member of the set S called i such that $i \oplus a = a$ for all a in the set S.
3. The associative law holds.
4. Corresponding to each element b in the set S there is an element b^{-1} in S such that

$$b^{-1} \oplus b = i.$$

It is evident that the set of even integers under addition forms a group, as does the set of all integers under addition. We assume that the associative law holds for all integers under addition and multiplication and that the set is closed as well.

Exercises

In the following assume that the associative law holds for all real numbers under addition and multiplication.

1. Prove that the set of all integers under addition forms a group. Does it under multiplication?

2. Prove that the set of rational numbers, except 0, forms a group under multiplication.

3. Does the set of numbers of the form $a + b\sqrt{3}$, with a and b integers, form a group under addition?

4. Is the set of numbers of the form $a + b\sqrt{3}$, a and b integers, closed under multiplication?

5. Is the set of numbers of the form $a + b\sqrt[3]{3} + c\sqrt[3]{9}$, a and b integers, closed under multiplication?

6. What is the inverse of the complex number $a + bi$, a and b real numbers, under addition? Under multiplication?

7. Given the three elements a, b and c with the following multiplication table (Table 1), prove that they form a group under multiplication:

Table 1

×	a	b	c
a	c	a	b
b	a	b	c
c	b	c	a

8. Construct a group of four elements a, b, c, d.

3. Some Basic Theorems

Now we shall prove some fundamental theorems concerning groups. We shall answer such questions as whether $i \oplus a = a \oplus i$. In other words is a left identity also a right identity? Also, is the identity unique? But, and most important of all, we shall determine under what conditions an equation involving only one operation can be assured of having a unique solution.

For convenience we introduce the use of the "member of" sign $\in$ as follows. If a belongs to the set S, we write $a \in S$.

If elements a, b and c belong to a set S, we write $a, b, c \in S$.

We shall use the capital letter G to refer to a group.

Theorem 1. If $a, b, c \in G$ and
$$c \oplus a = c \oplus b$$
then
$$a = b.$$

PROOF. By (4) of our definition of a group, there exists an element $c^{-1} \in G$ such that $c^{-1} \oplus c = i$.

$c^{-1} \oplus (c \oplus a) = c^{-1} \oplus (c \oplus b)$ Equals added to equals and closure.

$\therefore \quad (c^{-1} \oplus c) \oplus a = (c^{-1} \oplus c) \oplus b$ Associative law holds.

$\therefore \qquad\qquad i \oplus a = i \oplus b$ Property of inverse.

$\therefore \qquad\qquad\quad a = b$ Property of identity.

Theorem 1 is called the left-hand cancellation law.

Theorem 2. If $b \in G$, then
$$i \oplus b = b \oplus i = b.$$

PROOF. By (4) of our definition of a group, there exists an element $b^{-1} \in G$.

$b^{-1} \oplus (b \oplus i) = (b^{-1} \oplus b) \oplus i$ Associative law and closure.

$(b^{-1} \oplus b) \oplus i = i \oplus i$ Property of an inverse.

$i \oplus i = i = b^{-1} \oplus b$ Property of an identity and inverse.

$\therefore \quad b^{-1} \oplus (b \oplus i) = b^{-1} \oplus b$ Equals substituted for equals.

$\therefore \qquad\qquad b \oplus i = b$ Theorem 1.

This proves that the left identity is a right identity.

Theorem 3. If $b \in G$, then
$$b^{-1} \oplus b = b \oplus b^{-1} = i.$$

PROOF.

$b^{-1} \oplus (b \oplus b^{-1}) = (b^{-1} \oplus b) \oplus b^{-1}$ Associative law and closure.

$= i \oplus b^{-1}$ Property of an inverse.

$\therefore \quad b^{-1} \oplus (b \oplus b^{-1}) = b^{-1} \oplus i$ Theorem 2.

$\therefore \qquad\qquad b \oplus b^{-1} = i$ Theorem 1.

This proves that the left inverse is a right inverse.

Theorem 4. If $b, c \in G$, then the equations

(2) $b \oplus x = c$

and   (3) $y \oplus b = c$

have unique solutions in G.

PROOF. Equation (2) has a solution in G,

$$x = b^{-1} \oplus c,$$

since
$$b \oplus (b^{-1} \oplus c) = c.$$

Suppose equation (2) has two solutions x and x'. Then

$$b \oplus x = b \oplus x' = c$$
$$\therefore \quad x = x'$$

by Theorem 1, and the solution is unique.

In the same way equation (3) may be proved to have a unique solution in G.

From Theorem 4, we may prove that the identity i is unique for a group and that each element has a unique inverse.

We can conclude from Theorem 4 that every equation in which the elements are members of a group G, and in which there is a single operation, namely the operation under which the group is defined, always has a unique solution.

Note that this says nothing about solutions of an equation of the form $ax = b + c$ which involves two operations. We shall investigate this later.

It should be remarked that all of the preceding theorems could have been proven just as easily using any symbol for the operation, rather than $\oplus$. This symbol was selected only as a convenience and was not meant to imply that it even meant addition under the ordinary sense of the word. Many texts use the symbol for multiplication, whatever that may be. We might have called it little o.

Exercises

1. Prove the right-hand cancellation law for a group.
2. Complete the proof of Theorem 4.
3. Prove that the identity element of a group is unique.
4. Prove that each element of a group has a unique inverse.
5. Prove Theorems 1–4 using multiplication as the operation.
6. Why is there no distributive law for a group?

4. Finite Groups

To correct the possible impression that groups always have an infinite number of elements, we offer the following examples.

Suppose that we divide the set of integers into classes, or subsets, such that each class consists of members whose smallest nonnegative remainders, after division by some positive integer, are the same. For example, consider division by the integer 4. The class of integers whose remainder after division by 4 is 0 would be

$$[\ldots, -8, -4, 0, 4, 8, 12, \ldots] = C_0.$$

Those whose remainder after division by 4 is 1 would be
$$[\ldots, -7, -3, 1, 5, 9, \ldots] = C_1.$$
And similarly we have the classes
$$[\ldots, -10, -6, -2, 2, 6, 10, \ldots] = C_2$$
$$[\ldots, -9, -5, -1, 3, 7, 11, \ldots] = C_3.$$

Note that every integer belongs to one, and only one, of the four classes. If we now wish to add members of two classes and find the remainder which corresponds to the sum, it is only necessary to add the remainders. For example, $5 + 6 = 11$. But 11 has a remainder of 3 after division by 4. If we had added the remainders for 5 and 6, namely $1 + 2 = 3$, we would have obtained the same result.

Let us denote the set of remainders by
$$J_4: \{0, 1, 2, 3\}.$$

An addition table for these remainders would be as given in Table 2.

Table 2

+	0	1	2	3
0	0	1	2	3
1	1	2	3	0
2	2	3	0	1
3	3	0	1	2

We can now prove that the set J_4 forms a group under addition, since:

1. The set is closed under addition.
2. 0 is the identity element.
3. The associative law holds for all numbers under addition.
4. 0 is its own inverse, 1 is the inverse of 3 and 2 is its own inverse.

It is of importance to note that the set J_4 does not form a group under multiplication. The multiplication table would be as follows in Table 3.

Table 3

×	0	1	2	3
0	0	0	0	0
1	0	1	2	3
2	0	2	0	2
3	0	3	2	1

In checking it, the student should recall that, for example, $2 \times 2 = 4$; but $4 \in C_0$, and therefore $2 \times 2 = 0$. Similarly, $2 \times 3 = 6$, but $6 \in C_2$, and we have $2 \times 3 = 2$.

Notice that the inverse does not exist for 2, since there is no element b such that $2b = 1$ where 1 is the identity. There are a number of other ways in which this fails to be a group. These are left to the student to determine.

Now suppose we take the nonzero numbers of J_4 under multiplication. (See Table 4.)

Table 4

×	1	2	3
1	1	2	3
2	2	0	2
3	3	2	1

Our set is now not closed, and we do not have a group.

Notice again that a group depends both upon the operation under which it is defined and the members of the group.

For example, consider the nonzero remainders after division by 5 and under multiplication. Our set is

$$\{1, 2, 3, 4\}$$

where J_5 is: $\qquad \{0, 1, 2, 3, 4\}.$

Our multiplication table is shown in Table 5.

Table 5

×	1	2	3	4
1	1	2	3	4
2	2	4	1	3
3	3	1	4	2
4	4	3	2	1

We now have a group, since:

1. The set is closed.
2. 1 is the identity element.
3. The associative law holds.
4. 1 is its own inverse, 2 is the inverse of 3, 4 is its own inverse.

We can make a general statement, which we shall not prove. The set J_n forms a group under addition for all positive integers n. The nonzero members of J_n form a group under multiplication if and only if n is a prime number.

So we see that we have groups with any finite number of elements as well as those with an infinite number of elements. But let us veer away from the use of real numbers and integers in particular.

Consider the set of elements which are the fourth roots of unity, namely those elements x such that $x^4 = 1$. There are four of them $1, -1, i, -i$, where $i^2 = -1$. Note a difficulty which immediately arises. Here, we are using the symbol i to mean $i^2 = -1$. Previously, we used it to mean an identity element in a group. Some authors use the symbol e for the identity element, but they conflict with the use of e for the base of natural logarithms, among other things. The point to be made is that we may use any symbol or collection of symbols to stand for a quantity in a given problem; but it cannot represent two different quantities in the same problem or theorem, otherwise we run into contradictions. An author must carefully define his symbols as they are used in order to avoid confusion, just as we noted in the case of the symbol for an inverse. The student will run into many cases of duplicate symbols meaning different things. He needs to refer to the original use in order to be sure of the definition intended.

But in reference to our set $1, -1, i, -i$, clearly the elements are the four fourth roots of 1 since $1^4 = (-1)^4 = i^4 = (-i)^4 = 1$. Now taking multiplication as our operation we find our table becomes like Table 6.

Table 6

$\times$	1	-1	i	$-i$
1	1	-1	i	$-i$
-1	-1	1	$-i$	i
i	i	$-i$	-1	1
$-i$	$-i$	i	1	-1

The set forms a group under multiplication, since:

1. It is closed.
2. 1 is the identity.
3. The associative law holds.
4. 1 is its own inverse, -1 is its own inverse, i is inverse of $-i$ (and vice versa).

Now let us turn to an example from geometry. Take a square with two sides horizontal and vertices P_1, P_2, P_3 and P_4 as shown.

It is clear that a rotation of 90, 180, 270 and 360 degrees will leave the square in the original position with two sides horizontal. In the case of a rectangle some statement would have to be made as to whether the long or short sides are to be horizontal, and a rotation of 90 or 270 degrees would preserve neither.

Let us define a set S of the rotations of the square as follows.

RN $\leftrightarrow$ rotation of ninety degrees
ROE $\leftrightarrow$ rotation of one hundred eighty degrees
RTS $\leftrightarrow$ rotation of two hundred seventy degrees
I $\leftrightarrow$ rotation of three hundred sixty degrees.

We shall define the operation by which two elements of this set are combined as "followed by." For example, we write (ROE)(RN) = RTS as meaning a rotation of 90 degrees followed by a rotation of 180 degrees is the same as a rotation of 270 degrees. We shall use the regular product notation, although multiplication in the ordinary sense is not implied. We shall speak of the product of two elements of the set in this sense. All products are shown in Table 7.

Table 7

	I	RN	ROE	RTS
I	I	RN	ROE	RTS
RN	RN	ROE	RTS	I
ROE	ROE	RTS	I	RN
RTS	RTS	I	RN	ROE

The student should verify that the set S forms a group under this so-called product operation.

Exercises

1. J_4 divides all the integers into four distinct classes, corresponding to the remainders 0, 1, 2, 3. Prove the following.

(*a*) -7 has a remainder of 1 after division by 4.

(*b*) The sum of any member of the class with remainder 1 and any member of the class with remainder 2 is a member of the class with remainder 3.

2. Show that the set J_3 forms a group under addition and that the nonzero members form a group under multiplication. Why does not the set J_3 form a group under multiplication?

3. Does the set of nonzero members of J_6, under multiplication, form a group? State your reasons.

4. Is the set of fourth roots of unity a group under addition?

5. Define the set of rotations of an equilateral triangle. Is this set a group under some operation?

6. Find sets of one and two elements which form a group under some operation.

7. Make up a multiplication table for a group of three elements a, b and c. Is the answer unique except for the choice of letters?

5. Isomorphisms

Now, as examples, we have illustrated a number of groups with exactly four elements, but with different operations in some cases. First, the integers J_4 under addition. (These are sometimes called the integers modulo 4.) Second, the nonzero integers J_5 under multiplication. Third, the four fourth roots of unity under multiplication. Fourth, the rotations of a square under the product or "followed by" operation.

Since each of these groups has four elements, we may exhibit a one to one correspondence between their elements. But we wish to do more than this. We make the following definition.

Definition. Two groups G and G' with operations, say, $\oplus$ and $\otimes$, respectively, and elements $a, b, \ldots \in G$, $a', b', \ldots \in G'$, are said to be isomorphic if:

1. The elements can all be placed in a one to one correspondence as $a \leftrightarrow a'$, $b \leftrightarrow b'$, $\ldots$ and

2. If $a \leftrightarrow a'$ and $b \leftrightarrow b'$ then $a \oplus b \leftrightarrow a' \otimes b'$.

Such a correspondence shall be called an isomorphism.

For example, the integers modulo 4 under addition and the nonzero integers modulo 5 under multiplication are isomorphic as follows.

$$0 \leftrightarrow 1$$
$$1 \leftrightarrow 2$$
$$2 \leftrightarrow 4$$
$$3 \leftrightarrow 3.$$

To illustrate, we have
$$1 + 3 = 0$$
and
$$2 \times 3 = 1$$
and
$$0 \leftrightarrow 1.$$

Note that the identity elements correspond and each element which is its own inverse corresponds to an element in the other group which is its own inverse.

Theorem 5. The identity elements must correspond in any isomorphism.

PROOF. Assume $\qquad\qquad i \leftrightarrow a'$

and $\qquad\qquad\qquad b \leftrightarrow b';$

then $\quad i \oplus b \leftrightarrow a' \otimes b'$ By definition.

$\therefore \qquad b \leftrightarrow a' \otimes b'$ Property of an identity.

$\therefore \qquad a' = i'$ Correspondence must be one to one and $b \leftrightarrow b'$.

But an isomorphism is not necessarily unique, since we could have had
$$0 \leftrightarrow 1$$
$$1 \leftrightarrow 3$$
$$2 \leftrightarrow 4$$
$$3 \leftrightarrow 2.$$

Verification of an isomorphism can be accomplished by showing that the operation table of one group is obtained by substituting the corresponding elements in the table for the other group.

We further exhibit the isomorphisms.
$$0 \leftrightarrow 1 \leftrightarrow 1 \leftrightarrow I$$
$$1 \leftrightarrow 2 \leftrightarrow i \leftrightarrow RN$$
$$2 \leftrightarrow 4 \leftrightarrow -1 \leftrightarrow ROE$$
$$3 \leftrightarrow 3 \leftrightarrow -i \leftrightarrow RTS.$$

For example, in the first set we have
$$1 + 2 = 3.$$

In the second set, using corresponding elements,
$$2 \times 4 = 3.$$

In the third set, using corresponding elements,
$$(i)(-1) = -i.$$

And in the fourth set, using corresponding elements,
$$(RN)\,(ROE) = RTS.$$

But $\qquad\qquad 3 \leftrightarrow 3 \leftrightarrow -i \leftrightarrow RTS.$

The value of this set of isomorphisms is that a computation involving elements of one group may be replaced by the corresponding computation involving corresponding elements of another group. The answer is simply the element in the first group which corresponds to the result obtained in the second group. For example,

$$(i)^4(-i)^7(-1)^5 \leftrightarrow (1 + 1 + 1 + 1) + (3 + 3 + 3 + 3 + 3 + 3 + 3)$$
$$+ (2 + 2 + 2 + 2 + 2)$$
$$\leftrightarrow 0 + 1 + 2 = 3,$$

but $\qquad -i \leftrightarrow 3, \quad \therefore \quad (i)^4(-i)^7(-1)^5 = -i.$

There may be quite a difference between the operation in one group and that of another. If the groups are isomorphic, we do our computation in the group where the operation is the easiest to use.

Exercises

1. Find two isomorphisms between the group J_6 under addition and the nonzero members of J_7 under multiplication.

2. Is there another isomorphism between J_4 and the rotations of the square?

3. Is there another isomorphism between the nonzero members of J_5 and the fourth roots of unity?

4. In an isomorphism why must an element which is its own inverse correspond to a similar element in the other group? Prove your answer.

5. Compute $(RN)^3(ROE)(RTS)^4$ using the elements in the group of nonzero members of J_5 and also the fourth roots of unity.

6. Find two groups of three elements which are isomorphic.

7. What is the greatest number of different isomorphisms which could exist between two groups of four elements?

8. In an isomorphism, prove that if two elements correspond, then their inverses must correspond.

6. A Noncommutative Group

Frequently we number a set of objects and then have occasion to re-number them using the same set of integers. Such a rearrangement is called a **permutation** and may be represented symbolically, as in the following example.

$$\begin{pmatrix} 1 & 2 & 3 & 4 \\ 2 & 3 & 1 & 4 \end{pmatrix}.$$

The above symbol indicates that the object numbered 1 is now numbered 2. The object numbered 2 is now numbered 3. The object numbered 3 is now numbered 1. The object numbered 4 is still numbered 4.

This might represent, for example, the positions in which a set of four men finish in two races.

For greater convenience we shall write this symbol in **cyclic** notation as follows.

$$(123)(4).$$

Each cycle is enclosed in parentheses and is read from left to right until the last number is reached. Then we read the first number; in our example, we read "three becomes one." A number standing by itself means that it has not changed.

Thus the permutation

$$(251)(3)(4)$$

means that 2 becomes 5; 5 becomes 1; 1 becomes 2; 3 remains 3; 4 remains four.

But suppose that we follow one permutation by another. What is the result of such an operation? We shall refer to the operation as a product. For example, given

$$P_1 = (1423)$$
$$P_2 = (2431).$$

P_2P_1 means to follow P_1 by P_2, and we obtain

$$P_2P_1 = (132)(4).$$

This was obtained as follows. P_1 stated that 1 became 4. Then P_2 sent 4 into 3. Thus the net effect was to send 1 into 3. P_1 sent 3 into 1. Then P_2 sent 1 into 2 with the net effect of sending 3 into 2. The rest of the product can be verified in the same way. But now note the result if we compute P_1P_2.

We obtain

$$P_1P_2 = (134)(2) \neq P_2P_1.$$

This gives us an example of an operation in which the commutative law does not hold.

Let us demonstrate that the associative law does hold for three symbols and leave to the student the general proof that it holds for n symbols. Take

$$P_1 = \begin{pmatrix} 1 & 2 & 3 \\ a_1 & a_2 & a_3 \end{pmatrix}$$

$$P_2 = \begin{pmatrix} a_1 & a_2 & a_3 \\ b_1 & b_2 & b_3 \end{pmatrix}$$

$$P_3 = \begin{pmatrix} b_1 & b_2 & b_3 \\ c_1 & c_2 & c_3 \end{pmatrix}.$$

Then

$$P_2 P_1 = \begin{pmatrix} 1 & 2 & 3 \\ b_1 & b_2 & b_3 \end{pmatrix}$$

$$P_3(P_2 P_1) = \begin{pmatrix} 1 & 2 & 3 \\ c_1 & c_2 & c_3 \end{pmatrix}$$

But

$$P_3 P_2 = \begin{pmatrix} a_1 & a_2 & a_3 \\ c_1 & c_2 & c_3 \end{pmatrix}$$

$$(P_3 P_2) P_1 = \begin{pmatrix} 1 & 2 & 3 \\ c_1 & c_2 & c_3 \end{pmatrix} = P_3(P_2 P_1).$$

In cyclic notation it is easy to write the inverse of a permutation. We just reverse the order of the symbols. For example, if

$$P_1 = (1423)$$

then

$$P_1^{-1} = (3241)$$

and checking the product we find that

$$P_1^{-1} P_1 = (1)(2)(3)(4) = P_1 P_1^{-1} = I,$$

which is the identity permutation, which we shall denote by I, as indicated.

It can be proved that the $n!$ permutations on n symbols form a group, using the properties given above. We shall demonstrate this for the six permutations on three symbols.

But what does $n!$ (n factorial) mean? It is nothing more than a shorthand for the product of integers from n down to 1. For example,

$$5! = 5 \times 4 \times 3 \times 2 \times 1, \quad 4! = 4 \times 3 \times 2 \times 1.$$

We note that $5 \times 4! = 5!$ and in general $n(n - 1)! = n!$ According to this $1 \times 0! = 1!$ Therefore, we define $0! = 1$ for consistency. No definition exists for n a negative integer.

The six permutations on three symbols are as follows:

$$P_1 = (123); \quad P_2 = (132); \quad P_3 = (13)(2); \quad P_4 = (1)(23); \quad P_5 = (12)(3);$$
$$P_6 = (1)(2)(3) = I.$$

The table of multiplication for these is given in Table 8.

Note that the order of multiplication is to take an element from the first column, say P_5, as multiplier, and an element from the top row, say P_1, obtaining $P_5 P_1 = P_4$. Since the table is not symmetrical with respect to the diagonal running from upper left to lower right, the multiplication is not commutative. For example,

$$P_5P_1 \neq P_1P_5.$$

But further study of the table shows that each element has an inverse and that the set is closed under multiplication. Since the associative law

Table 8

	I	P_1	P_2	P_3	P_4	P_5
I	I	P_1	P_2	P_3	P_4	P_5
P_1	P_1	P_2	I	P_4	P_5	P_3
P_2	P_2	I	P_1	P_5	P_3	P_4
P_3	P_3	P_5	P_4	I	P_2	P_1
P_4	P_4	P_3	P_5	P_1	I	P_2
P_5	P_5	P_4	P_3	P_2	P_1	I

was proved for all permutations on 3 symbols, the set forms a group. Note that the subset I, P_1, P_2 also forms a group.

Definition. If a subset of a group forms a group under the same operation, it is called a subgroup.

Exercises

1. Prove that the subset I, P_1, P_2 of the example in the text forms a group.
2. Find the inverse of each element in the group of six permutations in the set.
3. (a) Find the solution of the equation $P_x P_2 = P_3$.
   (b) Solve $P_5 P_x = P_2$.
4. Find some other subgroups of the set of six permutations.
5. Prove that $P_1(P_2P_3) = (P_1P_2)P_3$ for all permutations on n symbols.
6. Find a subgroup of the twenty-four permutations on four symbols without finding all twenty-four.
7. Find the inverse of $P = (23)(617)(45)$. Prove that your result is correct.
8. Find another noncommutative group by considering the reflections of a square about its diagonals and its horizontal and vertical bisectors.
9. Can a group have one, two or three elements and be noncommutative?
10. What connection is there between the rotations and reflections of a square and the permutations on four symbols?

2 | MATRICES

1. Definitions

Now that we have found one important noncommutative operation let us find another. We turn to the solution of simultaneous equations. Here specific examples will not give us real clues to the operation which we seek as readily as the general case will do so. Therefore, consider the following pair of equations

$$x_1' = a_{11}x_1 + a_{12}x_2$$

(1)

$$x_2' = a_{21}x_1 + a_{22}x_2.$$

Note the use of subscripts, rather than using different letters, to distinguish not only between the coefficients but also between the variables themselves. Observe that we can readily locate the position of some coefficient or variable by its subscript or superscript, as in the case of x_1' and x_2'. We shall read x_1' and x_2' as x sub one prime and x sub two prime, respectively.

The set of equations (1) expresses the relation between the set of variables $\{x_1, x_2\}$ and the set $\{x_1', x_2'\}$. Let us consider a second set of equations as follows.

$$x_1'' = b_{11}x_1' + b_{12}x_2'$$

(2)

$$x_2'' = b_{21}x_1' + b_{22}x_2'.$$

This set of equations expresses the relation between the set of variables $\{x_1', x_2'\}$ and the set $\{x_1'', x_2''\}$, read x sub one double prime, x sub two double prime.

20

20

If we wished to find the relation between the set $\{x_1, x_2\}$ and the set $\{x_1'', x_2''\}$, we would substitute the values of x_1', x_2' from (1) into (2), obtaining

(3)
$$x_1'' = (b_{11}a_{11} + b_{12}a_{21})x_1 + (b_{11}a_{12} + b_{12}a_{22})x_2$$
$$x_2'' = (b_{21}a_{11} + b_{22}a_{21})x_1 + (b_{21}a_{12} + b_{22}a_{22})x_2.$$

Clearly (3) depends only on the position of the coefficients a_{11} etc., b_{11} etc., in the equations (1) and (2) and the position of the variables x_1, x_2, x_1', x_2'.

Definition. The matrix of coefficients of (1) shall be denoted by A and shall be the following square array.

$$A = \begin{pmatrix} a_{11} & a_{12} \\ a_{21} & a_{22} \end{pmatrix}$$

and in (2) as

$$B = \begin{pmatrix} b_{11} & b_{12} \\ b_{21} & b_{22} \end{pmatrix}.$$

Clearly A and B are symbols which have no numerical value. They are simply an array of numbers given in a certain position. We shall call each set of horizontal elements in A a row and each set of vertical elements a column. Under this definition the first subscript denotes the row in which an element appears, while the second subscript denotes the column in which an element appears.

This is another good reason for the subscript notation adopted earlier. Now (3) could be written in the form

$$x_1'' = c_{11}x_1 + c_{12}x_2$$
$$x_2'' = c_{21}x_1 + c_{22}x_2$$

where
$$c_{11} = b_{11}a_{11} + b_{12}a_{21}$$
$$c_{12} = b_{11}a_{12} + b_{12}a_{22}$$
$$c_{21} = b_{21}a_{11} + b_{22}a_{21}$$
$$c_{22} = b_{21}a_{12} + b_{22}a_{22}.$$

We write
$$C = \begin{pmatrix} c_{11} & c_{12} \\ c_{21} & c_{22} \end{pmatrix}$$

as the matrix of coefficients of (3).

Definition. We define a matrix of the variables by the array.

$$X = \begin{pmatrix} x_1 \\ x_2 \end{pmatrix}$$

and

$$X' = \begin{pmatrix} x_1' \\ x_2' \end{pmatrix}.$$

Definition. We shall write the equations (1), (2) and (3) in matrix form as follows.

(4)
$$\begin{pmatrix} x_1' \\ x_2' \end{pmatrix} = \begin{pmatrix} a_{11} & a_{12} \\ a_{21} & a_{22} \end{pmatrix} \begin{pmatrix} x_1 \\ x_2 \end{pmatrix}$$

(5)
$$\begin{pmatrix} x_1'' \\ x_2'' \end{pmatrix} = \begin{pmatrix} b_{11} & b_{12} \\ b_{21} & b_{22} \end{pmatrix} \begin{pmatrix} x_1' \\ x_2' \end{pmatrix}$$

(6)
$$\begin{pmatrix} x_1'' \\ x_2'' \end{pmatrix} = \begin{pmatrix} c_{11} & c_{12} \\ c_{21} & c_{22} \end{pmatrix} \begin{pmatrix} x_1 \\ x_2 \end{pmatrix}.$$

The primary object of this definition is to separate the coefficients from the variables in the equations in order that the effect of each may be studied separately. But such a definition is of no value unless we can put it to practical use in the solution of equations. Therefore, we substitute (4) into (5) obtaining

(7)
$$\begin{pmatrix} x_1'' \\ x_2'' \end{pmatrix} = \begin{pmatrix} b_{11} & b_{12} \\ b_{21} & b_{22} \end{pmatrix} \begin{pmatrix} a_{11} & a_{12} \\ a_{21} & a_{22} \end{pmatrix} \begin{pmatrix} x_1 \\ x_2 \end{pmatrix}.$$

Now recall that (6) also relates $\{x_1, x_2\}$ and $\{x_1'', x_2''\}$. Therefore, to be consistent we should have some definition whereby

$$\begin{pmatrix} b_{11} & b_{12} \\ b_{21} & b_{22} \end{pmatrix} \begin{pmatrix} a_{11} & a_{12} \\ a_{21} & a_{22} \end{pmatrix} = \begin{pmatrix} c_{11} & c_{12} \\ c_{21} & c_{22} \end{pmatrix}.$$

First, however, we must define what we shall mean by the equality of two matrices.

Definition. Two matrices shall be defined to be equal if each element of one is equal to the corresponding element of the other.

NOTE. This definition requires that two matrices have the same number of rows and the same number of columns in order to be equal.

Definition. Symbolically we find it convenient to write

$$A = (a_{ij}) \qquad \begin{array}{l} i = 1, 2, \ldots, n \\ j = 1, 2, \ldots, m \end{array}$$

to mean a matrix of n rows and m columns, where a_{ij} represents the element in the ith row and jth column. By using such a symbol we define, for two matrices A and B,

$$A = B$$

means $a_{ij} = b_{ij}$ $\begin{aligned} i &= 1, 2, \ldots, n \\ j &= 1, 2, \ldots, m. \end{aligned}$

Definition. The product of two matrices shall be a matrix such that if

$$B = (b_{ij}) \qquad \begin{aligned} i &= 1, 2, \ldots, n \\ j &= 1, 2, \ldots, m \end{aligned}$$

and $A = (a_{jk}) \qquad \begin{aligned} j &= 1, 2, \ldots, m \\ k &= 1, 2, \ldots, p \end{aligned}$

then $BA = C$

means $C = (c_{ik}) \qquad \begin{aligned} i &= 1, 2, \ldots, n \\ k &= 1, 2, \ldots, p \end{aligned}$

where $c_{ik} = b_{i1}a_{1k} + b_{i2}a_{2k} + b_{i3}a_{3k} + \cdots + b_{im}a_{mk}.$

NOTE. This definition requires that, in order for the product BA to be defined, the number of columns of B must be equal to the number of rows of A. There is no restriction on the number of rows of B or the number of columns of A.

As an illustration, consider the following example.

$$A = \begin{pmatrix} 2 & 3 \\ 1 & 4 \end{pmatrix} \quad \text{and} \quad B = \begin{pmatrix} 5 & 6 \\ 8 & 10 \end{pmatrix}$$

$$\therefore \quad BA = \begin{pmatrix} 5 \times 2 + & 6 \times 1 & 5 \times 3 + & 6 \times 4 \\ 8 \times 2 + & 10 \times 1 & 8 \times 3 + & 10 \times 4 \end{pmatrix}$$

$$\therefore \quad BA = \begin{pmatrix} 16 & 39 \\ 26 & 64 \end{pmatrix}.$$

We might have the case where one of the matrices had a different number of rows than columns. Suppose that

$$C = \begin{pmatrix} 3 & 4 \\ 2 & 7 \end{pmatrix} \quad \text{and} \quad D = \begin{pmatrix} 2 & 5 & 1 \\ 4 & 1 & 6 \end{pmatrix}.$$

Then $CD = \begin{pmatrix} 3 \times 2 + 4 \times 4 & 3 \times 5 + 4 \times 1 & 3 \times 1 + 4 \times 6 \\ 2 \times 2 + 7 \times 4 & 2 \times 5 + 7 \times 1 & 2 \times 1 + 7 \times 6 \end{pmatrix}$

$$\therefore \quad CD = \begin{pmatrix} 22 & 19 & 27 \\ 32 & 17 & 44 \end{pmatrix}.$$

It is evident that one would not use the formula for a product, given in the definition, in actual practice. The procedure is to multiply the elements in the first column of the matrix on the right by the corresponding elements of the first row of the matrix on the left, and then add these products. The sum is the element in the first row and first column of the product. (See the previous examples.)

Then we would multiply the elements in the second column of the matrix on the right by the corresponding elements of the first row of the matrix on the left, and then add these products. The sum is the element in the first row and second column of the product.

In other words, an element in the ith row and jth column of the product is obtained by multiplying the elements of the jth column of the matrix on the right by the corresponding elements of the ith row of the matrix on the left and then adding these products.

Exercises

1. Find the products indicated in each of the following cases:

(a) $$\begin{pmatrix} 2 & -5 \\ 8 & 1 \end{pmatrix}\begin{pmatrix} 3 & 4 \\ -2 & 6 \end{pmatrix}$$

(b) $$\begin{pmatrix} 1 & 0 \\ 0 & 1 \end{pmatrix}\begin{pmatrix} 5 & -4 \\ -1 & 7 \end{pmatrix}$$

(c) $$\begin{pmatrix} 6 & -2 \\ -1 & 8 \end{pmatrix}\begin{pmatrix} 3 \\ 10 \end{pmatrix}$$

2. Given the equations
$$x_1' = 2x_1 - x_2$$
$$x_2' = x_1 + 3x_2$$
and
$$x_1'' = x_1' + 2x_2'$$
$$x_2'' = 3x_1' - 2x_2',$$

write each pair of equations in matrix form; then write the relation between x_1'', x_2'' and x_1, x_2 in matrix form; and then compute the product of the matrices of the coefficients for the final form.

3. Find AB if
$$A = \begin{pmatrix} 2 & -3 & 4 \\ 1 & 2 & -1 \end{pmatrix}$$
and
$$B = \begin{pmatrix} 3 & 6 \\ 2 & 1 \\ 4 & -2 \end{pmatrix}.$$

4. Find AB if

$$A = \begin{pmatrix} 4 & 1 & -2 \\ 3 & 1 & 4 \\ -2 & 0 & 1 \end{pmatrix} \quad \text{and} \quad B = \begin{pmatrix} 2 & 3 \\ -1 & -2 \\ 4 & 1 \end{pmatrix}.$$

5. Find the conditions on the matrices A and B such that AB is a square matrix (has the same number of rows as columns).

6. If $A = \begin{pmatrix} 2 & a \\ b+1 & 3 \end{pmatrix}$ and $B = \begin{pmatrix} 2 & 3-b \\ a & 3 \end{pmatrix}$

find the values of a and b such that $A = B$.

7. If $A = (a_{ij})$ and $B = (b_{jk})$ $i = 1, 2; \, j = 1, 2; \, k = 1, 2$
find a_{ij} such that

$$AB = (c_{ij}) \quad\quad i = 1, 2; \, k = 1, 2$$

and

$$c_{ik} = 1 \quad \text{for} \quad i = k$$
$$c_{ik} = 0 \quad \text{for} \quad i \neq k.$$

8. Given $A = (a_{ij})$ and $B = (b_{ij})$ $i = 1, 2, \ldots, m$
                                              $j = 1, 2, \ldots, n$

we define the sum of the two matrices as

$$A + B = (a_{ij} + b_{ij}) \quad\quad i = 1, 2, \ldots, m$$
$$j = 1, 2, \ldots, n.$$

What additional conditions are required of matrices under addition that are not required under multiplication?

9. Given $A = \begin{pmatrix} 2 & 3 \\ 4 & 5 \end{pmatrix}$ and $B = \begin{pmatrix} -1 & 4 \\ 3 & -2 \end{pmatrix}$

find $A + B$, AB, $B + A$ and BA.

10. Find a matrix A such that $A + B = B$ for a given matrix B.

2. Properties of Products

To review, we note that in Section 1 of this chapter the product of the 2 by 2 matrices B and A was determined as follows. First, multiply the elements in the first column of A by the corresponding elements of the first row of B and then add the results, obtaining c_{11}. Next, multiply the elements in the second column of A by the corresponding elements in the first row of B and add the results, obtaining c_{12}. Next, multiply the elements in the first column of A by the corresponding elements in the second row of B and add the results, obtaining c_{21}. Finally, multiply the elements in the second column of A by the corresponding elements in the second row of B and add the results, obtaining c_{22}.

Now we find the product of the matrices A and X of Section 1, obtaining

$$AX = \begin{pmatrix} a_{11}x_1 + a_{12}x_2 \\ a_{21}x_1 + a_{22}x_2 \end{pmatrix}$$

Note that this product has two rows and only one column. But, from Section 1, we should have

$$AX = X',$$

therefore,

$$\begin{pmatrix} a_{11}x_1 + a_{12}x_2 \\ a_{21}x_1 + a_{22}x_2 \end{pmatrix} = \begin{pmatrix} x_1' \\ x_2' \end{pmatrix}.$$

From our definition of the equality of two matrices we obtain

$$a_{11}x_1 + a_{12}x_2 = x_1'$$
$$a_{21}x_1 + a_{22}x_2 = x_2'.$$

which is the set of equations (1) with which we started. Therefore, our definitions are consistent.

Perhaps the inquiring student now realizes why the matrix X was not defined as

$$X = (x_1 \; x_2)$$

instead of

$$\begin{pmatrix} x_1 \\ x_2 \end{pmatrix}$$

In symbolic form we now write the equations (4) as

$$X' = AX$$

and the equations (5) as

$$X'' = BX',$$

obtaining after substitution

$$X'' = B(AX) = (BA)X = CX$$

where we have assumed the associative law for matrices under multiplication. Although we shall not prove it here, this associative law can be readily proven in general by the definition of matrix products.

For example, to illustrate the associative law, we consider

$$\begin{pmatrix} 2 & 3 \\ -1 & 4 \end{pmatrix} \begin{pmatrix} 1 & -2 \\ -3 & 2 \end{pmatrix} \begin{pmatrix} -3 & -1 \\ 2 & 5 \end{pmatrix}$$

$$= \begin{pmatrix} 2 & 3 \\ -1 & 4 \end{pmatrix} \begin{pmatrix} -7 & -11 \\ 13 & 13 \end{pmatrix} = \begin{pmatrix} 25 & 17 \\ 59 & 63 \end{pmatrix}$$

or

$$= \begin{pmatrix} -7 & 2 \\ -13 & 10 \end{pmatrix} \begin{pmatrix} -3 & -1 \\ 2 & 5 \end{pmatrix} = \begin{pmatrix} 25 & 17 \\ 59 & 63 \end{pmatrix}.$$

With an example, we demonstrate that matrix multiplication does not satisfy the commutative law, that is, $BA \neq AB$.

Given:
$$B = \begin{pmatrix} 1 & 2 \\ -1 & 3 \end{pmatrix} \quad \text{and} \quad A = \begin{pmatrix} 2 & 5 \\ -3 & 4 \end{pmatrix}$$

$$BA = \begin{pmatrix} -4 & 13 \\ -11 & 7 \end{pmatrix}, \quad AB = \begin{pmatrix} -3 & 19 \\ -7 & 6 \end{pmatrix} \neq BA.$$

Notice the fundamental difference between the use of the two preceding examples. The first was simply the illustration of a law, indicating the possibility of a proof of the associative law. The second was a proof, by example, that the commutative law does not always hold.

Suppose we have the special matrix

$$I = \begin{pmatrix} 1 & 0 & 0 \\ 0 & 1 & 0 \\ 0 & 0 & 1 \end{pmatrix}$$

and consider its product with some other matrix

$$B = \begin{pmatrix} b_{11} & b_{12} \\ b_{21} & b_{22} \\ b_{31} & b_{32} \end{pmatrix},$$

we find that
$$IB = B.$$

In fact, if we take the matrix

$$C = \begin{pmatrix} c_{11} & c_{12} & c_{13} \\ c_{21} & c_{22} & c_{23} \\ c_{31} & c_{32} & c_{33} \end{pmatrix},$$

we find that
$$IC = C = CI.$$

In other words, if I and C have the properly related number of rows and columns, I behaves just like the identity element of a group under multiplication.

It should be noted that the preceding example does not imply that only a 3 by 3 matrix I can have this property. The number of rows and columns of I will depend upon the matrix which it multiplies. Therefore, the letter I cannot represent a unique matrix. Further properties are left for the exercises.

Exercises

1. Given the set of equations

$$x_1' = a_{11}x_1 + a_{12}x_2 + a_{13}x_3$$
$$x_2' = a_{21}x_1 + a_{22}x_2 + a_{23}x_3$$
$$x_3' = a_{31}x_1 + a_{32}x_2 + a_{33}x_3.$$

Write them in matrix form and then show, using the definition of products and equality, that the matrix form is consistent with the original set of equations.

2. Show that the commutative law for multiplication does not hold for the matrices

$$A = \begin{pmatrix} 3 & 4 \\ -2 & 6 \end{pmatrix} \quad \text{and} \quad B = \begin{pmatrix} 4 & 1 \\ 3 & 2 \end{pmatrix}.$$

3. Show that the commutative law for multiplication does hold for the matrices

$$A = \begin{pmatrix} 1 & -1 \\ 2 & 1 \end{pmatrix} \quad \text{and} \quad B = \begin{pmatrix} 2 & 1 \\ -2 & 2 \end{pmatrix}.$$

4. (a) Find the necessary and sufficient conditions that two 2 by 2 matrices be commutative under multiplication.

(b) Give an example of your results.

5. If I is the identity matrix, does $IC = CI$ whenever IC is valid? Give an example, if not.

6. (a) If $A = \begin{pmatrix} 2 & 3 \\ 4 & 5 \\ -6 & 2 \end{pmatrix}$ find IA.

(b) If $B = \begin{pmatrix} 3 & 4 & 2 \\ 6 & 8 & 1 \end{pmatrix}$ find IB.

7. Prove that I is the matrix

$$I = (a_{ij}) \qquad i = 1, 2, \ldots, n$$
$$j = 1, 2, \ldots, n.$$

where

$$a_{ij} = 1 \qquad i = j$$
$$a_{ij} = 0 \qquad i \neq j.$$

8. If I is a 3 by 3 matrix, show that $II = I$.

9. We define the product of a real number c and matrix A, where

$$A = (a_{ij}), \quad \text{as} \quad cA = (ca_{ij}) \qquad i = 1, 2, \ldots, n$$
$$j = 1, 2, \ldots, m.$$

(a) What is the matrix $2I$?

(b) What is the result of multiplying the matrix

$$A = (a_{ij}) \qquad i = 1, 2, \ldots, n$$
$$j = 1, 2, \ldots, m$$

by the matrix $2I$?

(c) What is the result of multiplying by the matrix $(-1)I$?

3. Inverse of a Matrix

Definition. The order of a square matrix is the number of rows (or columns).

NOTE. The term order does not apply to matrices which are not square.

The existence of an identity matrix I leads to the question of whether or not, for a given matrix A of order n, there is an inverse matrix A^{-1} under multiplication. An example will illustrate the existence of such an inverse in at least certain cases.

$$\begin{pmatrix} 2 & 1 \\ 1 & -1 \end{pmatrix} \begin{pmatrix} 1/3 & 1/3 \\ 1/3 & -2/3 \end{pmatrix} = \begin{pmatrix} 1 & 0 \\ 0 & 1 \end{pmatrix}$$

and

$$\begin{pmatrix} 1/3 & 1/3 \\ 1/3 & -2/3 \end{pmatrix} \begin{pmatrix} 2 & 1 \\ 1 & -1 \end{pmatrix} = \begin{pmatrix} 1 & 0 \\ 0 & 1 \end{pmatrix}.$$

We have indicated a case where it is evident that not only does the inverse of a matrix exist, but also the commutative law holds for the product of the matrix and its inverse.

Definition. The inverse of a given matrix A shall be the matrix A^{-1} such that

$$A^{-1}A = AA^{-1} = I$$

Note that this definition restricts the question of an inverse to square matrices.

But the existence of a definition does not insure the existence of an inverse for any given matrix. Let us consider the problem in general for a matrix of order 2.

Given the matrix

$$A = \begin{pmatrix} a_{11} & a_{12} \\ a_{21} & a_{22} \end{pmatrix},$$

we ask for a matrix

$$B = \begin{pmatrix} b_{11} & b_{12} \\ b_{21} & b_{22} \end{pmatrix}$$

such that $BA = AB = I$. Therefore,

$$\begin{pmatrix} b_{11} & b_{12} \\ b_{21} & b_{22} \end{pmatrix} \begin{pmatrix} a_{11} & a_{12} \\ a_{21} & a_{22} \end{pmatrix} = \begin{pmatrix} 1 & 0 \\ 0 & 1 \end{pmatrix}.$$

By performing the indicated multiplication one finds, using the definition of equality, that

$$b_{11}a_{11} + b_{12}a_{21} = 1$$
$$b_{11}a_{12} + b_{12}a_{22} = 0$$
$$b_{21}a_{11} + b_{22}a_{21} = 0$$
$$b_{21}a_{12} + b_{22}a_{22} = 1.$$

(8)

Since the a_{ij} are given, it is evident that the first pair of the set of equations (8) will give the solutions for b_{11} and b_{12}, and the second pair will give the solutions for b_{21} and b_{22}, if the solutions exist.

It is further evident that the first pair of equations have the same set of coefficients, a_{11}, a_{21}, a_{12}, a_{22}, as the second pair and in the same corresponding positions. Therefore, if there is a solution for the first pair, there must be a solution for the second pair. However, these solutions may not be the same for each pair of equations, since the constant terms are not the same values in the same positions. (See exercises for various possibilities.)

For one who is familiar with determinants we remark that the necessary and sufficient condition that these equations have a solution is that

$$\begin{vmatrix} a_{11} & a_{12} \\ a_{21} & a_{22} \end{vmatrix} \neq 0.$$

Whether or not one is familiar with determinants the necessary and sufficient condition is that the pair $(a_{11}\ a_{12})$ not be some multiple of the pair $(a_{21},\ a_{22})$, such as $(2, 5)$ and $(1, \frac{5}{2})$ where the first pair is obtained by multiplying each member of the second pair by two, or the second pair is obtained by multiplying each member of the first pair by $\frac{1}{2}$.

Therefore, some matrices of order 2, those satisfying the conditions above, have a unique inverse, and all others do not.

Definition. If an nth order matrix A has an inverse, A^{-1}, then A is said to be nonsingular. Otherwise it is called singular.

The necessary and sufficient conditions for a second order matrix to have an inverse need to be generalized to cover matrices of the nth order. We digress for a moment to establish some properties which will be used in generalizing the conditions above.

Definition. Given a set S containing elements $a_1, a_2, a_3, \ldots, a_n$, we say say that an element b, belonging to S, can be expressed as a linear combination of the elements $a_1, a_2, \ldots, a_n$ if there are elements $c_1, c_2, \ldots, c_n$, not necessarily belonging to S but to some set R, such that

$$b = c_1a_1 + c_2a_2 + c_3a_3 + \cdots + c_na_n.$$

Furthermore, the set $a_1, a_2, \ldots, a_n$ is said to be linearly independent over the set R if

$$c_1 a_1 + c_2 a_2 + c_3 a_3 + \cdots + c_n a_n = 0, \qquad 0 \in S$$

implies that $\qquad c_1 = c_2 = c_3 = \cdots = c_n = 0. \qquad 0 \in R$

Otherwise they are said to be linearly dependent over the set R.

EXAMPLE. Let S be the set consisting of 0 and the 4th roots of unity, namely $1, -1, i, -i$. Let R be the set of integers. Can

$$1 = c_1(-1) + c_2(i)?$$

The answer is yes, if $c_1 = -1$ and $c_2 = 0$. Therefore, 1 can be expressed as a linear combination of -1 and i. Can

$$i = c_1(1) + c_2(-1)?$$

The answer is no, for the sum of two integers is obviously never an imaginary number.

Are i and 1 linearly independent? The answer is yes, since

$$c_1(i) + c_2(1) = 0$$

implies $\qquad\qquad\qquad c_1 = c_2 = 0.$

Otherwise $\qquad\qquad\qquad c_2 = -c_1(i).$

But c_2 is an integer and $-c_1(i)$ is not.

Now we state the following theorem.

Theorem 1. Given the set of n linear equations in n unknowns

$$a_{11}x_1 + a_{12}x_2 + \cdots + a_{1n}x_n = b_1$$
$$a_{21}x_1 + a_{22}x_2 + \cdots + a_{2n}x_n = b_2$$
$$\cdots$$
$$a_{n1}x_1 + a_{n2}x_2 + \cdots + a_{nn}x_n = b_n,$$

(9)

there is a unique solution if and only if

(10) $\qquad c_1(a_{11}, a_{12}, \ldots, a_{1n}) + c_2(a_{21}, a_{22}, \ldots, a_{2n}) + \cdots$
$$+ c_n(a_{n1}, a_{n2}, \ldots, a_{nn}) = (0, 0, \ldots, 0)$$

implies $\qquad\qquad\qquad c_1 = c_2 = \cdots = c_n = 0.$

We shall not give a formal proof, but let us look at some of the possibilities. If condition (10) holds with at least one c_i not zero, then one could find the set of coefficients of some equation as a linear combination of some of the other sets of coefficients. Therefore, by legitimate multiplication of certain of these equations by constants, followed by additions to others, we could change all the coefficients of one equation to zero. If the constant term were not also zero, we would have a contradiction, meaning no possible solution to the set of equations. If the constant term were zero, we would have left a system of $(n-1)$ equations and n unknowns with an infinite number of solutions or none.

EXAMPLE.
$$x_1 + x_2 - 2x_3 = 1$$
$$2x_1 - x_2 + x_3 = -4$$
$$4x_1 + x_2 - 3x_3 = 3.$$

Set $c_1(1, 1, -2) + c_2(2, -1, 1) + c_3(4, 1, -3) = (0, 0, 0)$. This holds if $c_1 = 2$ and $c_2 = 1$ and $c_3 = -1$. Now multiply the first equation by 2 and add it to the second equation and the system becomes

$$x_1 + x_2 - 2x_3 = 1$$
$$4x_1 + x_2 - 3x_3 = -2$$
$$4x_1 + x_2 - 3x_3 = 3.$$

Now multiply the second equation by -1 and add it to the third equation and our system becomes

$$x_1 + x_2 - 2x_3 = 1$$
$$4x_1 + x_2 - 3x_3 = -2$$
$$0x_1 + 0x_2 + 0x_3 = 5.$$

Obviously the last equation is impossible, and our set of equations can have no solution (x_1, x_2, x_3) which satisfies all three equations.

Now if the original constant term in the third equation has been -2, the student can observe that the above result would have been

$$x_1 + x_2 - 2x_3 = 1$$
$$4x_1 + x_2 - 3x_3 = -2$$
$$0x_1 + 0x_2 + 0x_3 = 0$$

which has an infinite number of solutions (x_1, x_2, x_3).

Therefore, we make the following definition.

Definition. The rank r of a matrix shall be the greatest number of linearly independent rows.

For an example, consider the following third order matrix:

$$\begin{pmatrix} 2 & 3 & 5 \\ 4 & 6 & 1 \\ 14 & 21 & 17 \end{pmatrix}$$

The first and second rows are linearly independent, since the second row is not a multiple of the first. It is evident that the first two elements in the second row, 4 and 6, are twice the corresponding elements in the first row, but the third element, 1, is not twice the third element in the first row.

Therefore, the rank of the matrix, by the definition, is at least 2. We now ask whether all three rows are linearly independent. If so, the rank is 3. We write

$$c_1(2, 3, 5) + c_2(4, 6, 1) + c_3(14, 21, 17) = (0, 0, 0)$$

The question is as to whether or not $c_1 = c_2 = c_3 = 0$ is the only set of values for which this is true. The answer in this case is no, since

$$c_1 = 3, c_2 = 2, c_3 = -1$$

will also work.

Therefore, these three rows are linearly dependent and the rank of the matrix is 2.

The next theorem follows directly from Theorem 1.

Theorem 2. A set of n linear equations in n unknowns has a unique solution if and only if the rank r of the matrix of its coefficients is equal to the order of the matrix, i.e., $r = n$.

COROLLARY: An nth order matrix has an inverse if and only if the rank is equal to the order of the matrix.

Theorem 2 is only a restatement of Theorem 1, using the definition of rank.

To prove the corollary we remark that an nth order matrix A has an inverse B of nth order if and only if

$$AB = BA = I$$

where I is the identity matrix of order n.

Multiplying the two matrices and equating corresponding elements in the matrix equation for the first columns on each side, one obtains

$$a_{11}b_{11} + a_{12}b_{21} + \cdots + a_{1n}b_{n1} = 1$$
$$a_{21}b_{11} + a_{22}b_{21} + \cdots + a_{2n}b_{n1} = 0$$
$$a_{31}b_{11} + a_{32}b_{21} + \cdots + a_{3n}b_{n1} = 0$$
$$\cdots$$
$$a_{n1}b_{11} + a_{n2}b_{21} + \cdots + a_{nn}b_{n1} = 0.$$

Here, the a's are known and b's are unknown. From Theorem 2 there is a unique solution if and only if the matrix of the coefficients has rank

$r = n$. But the matrix of the coefficients is A, and so the rank of A must equal the order of A.

In the same way, equating the corresponding elements on each side in each column we will obtain n simultaneous equations, but in each set the matrix of the coefficients will be the same matrix A. By using Theorem 2, each time we reach the same conclusion for the conditions on the matrix A.

The student should write out several of the cases to satisfy himself.

Exercises

1. If $A = \begin{pmatrix} 2 & 3 \\ -4 & -3 \end{pmatrix}$ find A^{-1} and check your result.

2. If $A = \begin{pmatrix} 2 & 1 \\ 4 & 2 \end{pmatrix}$ show that it has no inverse.

3. Let $S = \{0, 1, -1, i, -i\}$, and let R be the set of integers.
   (a) Can -1 be expressed as a linear combination of 1 and i over R?
   (b) Are i and $-i$ linearly independent?
   (c) Are $-i$ and -1 linearly independent?
   (d) Can $-i$ be expressed as a linear combination of 1, -1, i and $-i$?

4. Given the set $S = \{1, x, x^2, x^3\}$, where x is any real number and R the set of integers.
   (a) Is the set S linearly independent over R for all x?
   (b) If x is any integer modulo 4, is S linearly independent over R?

5. What is the rank of the matrix

$$A = \begin{pmatrix} 1 & 2 & 1 \\ 2 & 1 & -2 \\ 4 & 5 & 0 \end{pmatrix} ?$$

6. Show that the following matrix is nonsingular and find its inverse.

$$\begin{pmatrix} 2 & -3 & 1 \\ 1 & 2 & -4 \\ 4 & -1 & 3 \end{pmatrix}.$$

7. What is the rank of the matrix

$$\begin{pmatrix} 3 & 4 & 2 \\ 6 & 8 & 4 \\ -9 & -12 & -6 \end{pmatrix} ?$$

8. Give an example of a set of 3 equations:
   (a) That has a unique solution according to Theorem 2.
   (b) That does not have a unique solution.

4. Elementary Row Operations

We turn to the numerical solution of simultaneous equations. From our definitions above, the following pair of equations

(11)
$$2x_1 + x_2 = 3$$
$$x_1 - x_2 = 6$$

may be written in matrix form as follows.

(12)
$$\begin{pmatrix} 2 & 1 \\ 1 & -1 \end{pmatrix} \begin{pmatrix} x_1 \\ x_2 \end{pmatrix} = \begin{pmatrix} 3 \\ 6 \end{pmatrix}.$$

From algebra we can see that the following operations on (11) will not change the solutions of the equations.

1. Multiplication of both sides of an equation by a nonzero constant.
2. Interchange of the equations.
3. Replacement of an equation by the sum of the equation and another equation.

For an example of operation 3 consider the effect on (11) of replacing the second equation by its sum taken with the first equation, obtaining

$$2x_1 + x_2 = 3$$
$$3x_1 + 0x_2 = 9.$$

Observe that the second equation gives $x_1 = 3$ and then from the first, $x_2 = -3$ which is the solution of (11), as can be readily checked.

These are just the basic operations, with which we are familiar, as used in solving simultaneous equations. But, note this carefully, none of these operations changed the position of the variables in the equations in any way.

Therefore, we ask what similar operations could have been made upon the matrices of the coefficients and the constants in (12) and not have changed the validity of the matrix equations.

Definition. The three "elementary row operations" on a matrix are as follows.

1. Multiplication of the elements of a row by a nonzero constant.
2. Interchange of all of the corresponding elements of two rows.
3. Replacement of the elements of a given row by the sum of its elements with the corresponding elements of another row.

Naturally any one of these operations will change a matrix, but if the same operation, or combination of operations, is used on the matrices on each side of a matrix equation the solution of the equations will still be the same. In the following example notice that the matrix of variables remains unchanged.

For example, we take the equation (12)

$$\begin{pmatrix} 2 & 1 \\ 1 & -1 \end{pmatrix} \begin{pmatrix} x_1 \\ x_2 \end{pmatrix} \begin{pmatrix} 3 \\ 6 \end{pmatrix}$$

and using row operation 2 we have

$$\begin{pmatrix} 1 & -1 \\ 2 & 1 \end{pmatrix} \begin{pmatrix} x_1 \\ x_2 \end{pmatrix} = \begin{pmatrix} 6 \\ 3 \end{pmatrix}.$$

By using operation 3 we multiply the elements of row one by -2 and add the results to row two, obtaining

$$\begin{pmatrix} 1 & -1 \\ 0 & 3 \end{pmatrix} \begin{pmatrix} x_1 \\ x_2 \end{pmatrix} = \begin{pmatrix} 6 \\ -9 \end{pmatrix}.$$

Now using operation 1 we multiply the elements of row two by $\frac{1}{3}$, obtaining

$$\begin{pmatrix} 1 & -1 \\ 0 & 1 \end{pmatrix} \begin{pmatrix} x_1 \\ x_2 \end{pmatrix} = \begin{pmatrix} 6 \\ -3 \end{pmatrix}.$$

Using operation 3 we add row two to row one, obtaining

$$\begin{pmatrix} 1 & 0 \\ 0 & 1 \end{pmatrix} \begin{pmatrix} x_1 \\ x_2 \end{pmatrix} = \begin{pmatrix} 3 \\ -3 \end{pmatrix}.$$

But now the matrix product on the left is easily obtained, using the property of the identity matrix, and we have

$$\begin{pmatrix} x_1 \\ x_2 \end{pmatrix} = \begin{pmatrix} 3 \\ -3 \end{pmatrix}.$$

Then by the definition of the equality of two matrices we have

$$x_1 = 3 \quad \text{and} \quad x_2 = -3,$$

which is the solution of the original equations (11), as can be verified by direct substitution.

No claim is made that this method is faster than any traditional approach to this problem, by elimination of variables. What is claimed is that this procedure can be generalized to n equations with n unknowns and will result in an orderly process of finding the solution, by hand or with the aid of a computer.

Exercises

1. Using successive elementary row operations change the matrix

$$A = \begin{pmatrix} 2 & 3 \\ -4 & 1 \end{pmatrix}$$

into the identity matrix. Therefore, prove that an elementary row operation on some matrix A, alone, will in general change the matrix equation

$$A = B$$

into

$$C \neq B.$$

2. Show that the matrix

$$\begin{pmatrix} 2 & 4 \\ 1 & 2 \end{pmatrix}$$

cannot be changed into the identity matrix by elementary row operations.

3. Find the matrix which results from using the same elementary row operations in problem 1 on the second order identity matrix. Call the result B and find BA.

4. (a) Write the following equations in matrix form and solve using elementary row operations.

$$5x + 3y = 4$$
$$2x - 4y = 3.$$

(b) Change the constant terms to 3 and 4, respectively, and show that the solution changes. Could the solutions be the same for any case with a different pair of constant terms?

5. By successive elementary row operations change the matrix

$$A = \begin{pmatrix} 2 & 3 & 4 \\ -1 & 5 & 8 \\ 5 & 14 & 20 \end{pmatrix}$$

into a matrix

$$B = \begin{pmatrix} 1 & b_{12} & b_{13} \\ 0 & b_{22} & b_{23} \\ 0 & b_{32} & b_{33} \end{pmatrix}$$

finding

$$b_{ij} \qquad i = 1, 2, 3$$
$$j = 2, 3.$$

6. (a) Is there any matrix of order 2 which can be changed into the matrix

$$C = \begin{pmatrix} 0 & 0 \\ 0 & 0 \end{pmatrix}?$$

by elementary row operations.

(b) Can matrix C be changed into any other matrix by elementary row operations?

5. Gauss-Jordan Process

In order to develop an orderly process whereby we might solve n equations with n unknowns, we first write our equations in matrix form as follows.

$$AX = B$$

where
$$A = (a_{ij}) \qquad i = 1, 2, \ldots, n$$
$$j = 1, 2, \ldots, n$$
$$X = (x_j) \qquad j = 1, 2, \ldots, n \qquad B = (b_i) \qquad i = 1, 2, \ldots, n$$
$$\text{(column matrix)} \qquad\qquad \text{(column matrix).}$$

We know that we may operate on both sides of the matrix equation above using the same elementary row operations. If, by a sequence of such operations, we can change the matrix A into the matrix I we will obtain the equation

$$IX = C,$$

where C is the result of applying the same sequence of elementary row operations to B as were applied to A. Since

$$IX = X$$

we obtain
$$X = C$$

and using the property of equality of two matrices we obtain as our solution

$$x_i = c_i, \qquad i = 1, 2, \ldots, n.$$

But what sequence of operations shall we use to change the matrix A to the matrix I? We recall, of course, that our goal is to end up with unity in the position $a_{ii}, i = 1, 2, \ldots, n$, and zero everywhere else. We proceed as follows. (The student may wish to look ahead to the example on page 39, while reading.)

We observe whether the element a_{11} is zero or not. If it is zero we interchange the first row with the nearest row below it for which the first element is not zero (row operation 2). If there is no such row then the rows are linearly dependent and the rank r is less than n and the equations do not have a unique solution. Then we stop the process.

If a_{11} is not zero, or after we replace it by a nonzero element, as indicated above, we multiply the first row by the reciprocal of a_{11} (row operation 1).

Next we replace the second row by its sum taken with the first row, after the first row has been multiplied by the negative of the first element in the second row (row operation 3). This will change the first element in the second row to zero.

We continue in the same way, replacing the ith row by its sum taken with the first row after the first row has been multiplied by the negative of the first element in the ith row. This will change the first element in the ith row to zero.

We continue until there is a zero as the first element in the nth row.

Then we observe whether the element a_{22} is zero or not. If it is zero, we interchange the second row with the nearest row below it for which the second element is not zero. If there is no such row, then the rows are linearly dependent and we stop the process.

We make two comments here. First, interchanging the second row with any row below it will not affect the zero as the first element. Second, we would not interchange with the row above as this would destroy all of our previous efforts.

Now, if a_{22} is not zero, or after we replace it by a nonzero element, as indicated above, we multiply the second row by the reciprocal of a_{22}, changing a_{22} to unity.

Next, we replace the first row by its sum taken with the second row after the second row has been multiplied by the negative of the second element in the first row. This will change the second element in the first row to zero. But note that this step will not affect the first element which has already been changed to unity, since it will be added to zero.

Then for each row i below the second row, $i = 3, 4, \ldots, n$, we replace the ith row by its sum taken with the second row after the second row has been multiplied by the negative of the second element in the ith row. This will change the second element in the ith row to zero, without affecting the first element which is already zero.

It is left to the student as an exercise to write a general statement for the procedure for any row.

It is evident that, except for the case of linear dependence of the rows, the procedure will change the matrix A into the matrix I.

It is remembered that the same operations are to be applied in the same sequence to the matrix B, obtaining the matrix C of the solution.

Let us consider a particular case with three unknowns and develop an additional property of this method. We take the equations

$$2x_1 - 3x_2 + x_3 = 10$$
$$x_1 + 2x_2 - 4x_3 = -11$$
$$4x_1 - x_2 + 3x_3 = 12$$

and write the matrix equation as

$$\begin{pmatrix} 2 & -3 & 1 \\ 1 & 2 & -4 \\ 4 & -1 & 3 \end{pmatrix} \begin{pmatrix} x_1 \\ x_2 \\ x_3 \end{pmatrix} = \begin{pmatrix} 10 \\ -11 \\ 12 \end{pmatrix}.$$

Now before attempting to solve we will write the right-hand side, using the properties of the identity matrix, as

$$\begin{pmatrix} 2 & -3 & 1 \\ 1 & 2 & -4 \\ 4 & -1 & 3 \end{pmatrix} \begin{pmatrix} x_1 \\ x_2 \\ x_3 \end{pmatrix} = \begin{pmatrix} 1 & 0 & 0 \\ 0 & 1 & 0 \\ 0 & 0 & 1 \end{pmatrix} \begin{pmatrix} 10 \\ -11 \\ 12 \end{pmatrix}.$$

Therefore, when we proceed to reduce the matrix of the coefficients to the identity matrix, we note that we have two choices as to the matrix on the right-hand side on which we shall apply our row operations.

We shall take both cases, the first operating on the identity matrix and the second operating on the matrix of the constants. So we write

$$\begin{pmatrix} 2 & -3 & 1 \\ 1 & 2 & -4 \\ 4 & -1 & 3 \end{pmatrix} \begin{pmatrix} x_1 \\ x_2 \\ x_3 \end{pmatrix} = \begin{pmatrix} 1 & 0 & 0 \\ 0 & 1 & 0 \\ 0 & 0 & 1 \end{pmatrix} \begin{pmatrix} 10 \\ -11 \\ 12 \end{pmatrix} = \begin{pmatrix} 1 & 0 & 0 \\ 0 & 1 & 0 \\ 0 & 0 & 1 \end{pmatrix} \begin{pmatrix} 10 \\ -11 \\ 12 \end{pmatrix}.$$

We recall that we wish to change the matrix of the coefficients into the identity matrix. We start with the element in the first row and first column. If it were zero, we would interchange the row with some other row in which the first element is not zero. If this is impossible, there is no solution by this method.

Since the element is not zero, we multiply the first row by the reciprocal of the first element in order that the resulting value of the first element shall be unity (row operation 1), obtaining

$$\begin{pmatrix} 1 & -3/2 & 1/2 \\ 1 & 2 & -4 \\ 4 & -1 & 3 \end{pmatrix} \begin{pmatrix} x_1 \\ x_2 \\ x_3 \end{pmatrix} = \begin{pmatrix} 1/2 & 0 & 0 \\ 0 & 1 & 0 \\ 0 & 0 & 1 \end{pmatrix} \begin{pmatrix} 10 \\ -11 \\ 12 \end{pmatrix} = \begin{pmatrix} 1 & 0 & 0 \\ 0 & 1 & 0 \\ 0 & 0 & 1 \end{pmatrix} \begin{pmatrix} 5 \\ -11 \\ 12 \end{pmatrix}.$$

Now we wish to obtain zeros in all other positions in the first column. Therefore, we multiply the elements in the first row by the negative of the first element in the second row and add the results to the second row, leaving the first row unchanged (row operation 3), obtaining

$$\begin{pmatrix} 1 & -3/2 & 1/2 \\ 0 & 7/2 & -9/2 \\ 4 & -1 & 3 \end{pmatrix} \begin{pmatrix} x_1 \\ x_2 \\ x_3 \end{pmatrix} = \begin{pmatrix} 1/2 & 0 & 0 \\ -1/2 & 1 & 0 \\ 0 & 0 & 1 \end{pmatrix} \begin{pmatrix} 10 \\ -11 \\ 12 \end{pmatrix}$$
$$= \begin{pmatrix} 1 & 0 & 0 \\ 0 & 1 & 0 \\ 0 & 0 & 1 \end{pmatrix} \begin{pmatrix} 5 \\ -16 \\ 12 \end{pmatrix}.$$

In the same way we multiply the elements in the first row by the negative of the first element in the third row and add the results to the third row, obtaining

$$\begin{pmatrix} 1 & -3/2 & 1/2 \\ 0 & 7/2 & -9/2 \\ 0 & 5 & 1 \end{pmatrix} \begin{pmatrix} x_1 \\ x_2 \\ x_3 \end{pmatrix} = \begin{pmatrix} 1/2 & 0 & 0 \\ -1/2 & 1 & 0 \\ -2 & 0 & 1 \end{pmatrix} \begin{pmatrix} 10 \\ -11 \\ 12 \end{pmatrix}$$

$$= \begin{pmatrix} 1 & 0 & 0 \\ 0 & 1 & 0 \\ 0 & 0 & 1 \end{pmatrix} \begin{pmatrix} 5 \\ -16 \\ -8 \end{pmatrix}.$$

Now we consider the element in the second row and second column (namely 7/2). Since it is not zero, and we wish it to be unity, we multiply the elements in the second row by the reciprocal of that element (namely 2/7) (row operation 1), obtaining

$$\begin{pmatrix} 1 & -3/2 & 1/2 \\ 0 & 1 & -9/7 \\ 0 & 5 & 1 \end{pmatrix} \begin{pmatrix} x_1 \\ x_2 \\ x_3 \end{pmatrix} = \begin{pmatrix} 1/2 & 0 & 0 \\ -1/7 & 2/7 & 0 \\ -2 & 0 & 1 \end{pmatrix} \begin{pmatrix} 10 \\ -11 \\ 12 \end{pmatrix}$$

$$= \begin{pmatrix} 1 & 0 & 0 \\ 0 & 1 & 0 \\ 0 & 0 & 1 \end{pmatrix} \begin{pmatrix} 5 \\ -32/7 \\ -8 \end{pmatrix}.$$

Since we wish all other elements in the second column to be zero, we multiply the elements in the second row by the negative of the second element in the first row and add to the first row, obtaining

$$\begin{pmatrix} 1 & 0 & -10/7 \\ 0 & 1 & -9/7 \\ 0 & 5 & 1 \end{pmatrix} \begin{pmatrix} x_1 \\ x_2 \\ x_3 \end{pmatrix} = \begin{pmatrix} 2/7 & 3/7 & 0 \\ -1/7 & 2/7 & 0 \\ -2 & 0 & 1 \end{pmatrix} \begin{pmatrix} 10 \\ -11 \\ 12 \end{pmatrix}$$

$$= \begin{pmatrix} 1 & 0 & 0 \\ 0 & 1 & 0 \\ 0 & 0 & 1 \end{pmatrix} \begin{pmatrix} -13/7 \\ -32/7 \\ -8 \end{pmatrix}.$$

Then we multiply the elements in the second row by the negative of the second element in the third row and add to the third row, obtaining

$$
\begin{pmatrix} 1 & 0 & -10/7 \\ 0 & 1 & -9/7 \\ 0 & 0 & 52/7 \end{pmatrix} \begin{pmatrix} x_1 \\ x_2 \\ x_3 \end{pmatrix} = \begin{pmatrix} 2/7 & 3/7 & 0 \\ -1/7 & 2/7 & 0 \\ -9/7 & -10/7 & 1 \end{pmatrix} \begin{pmatrix} 10 \\ -11 \\ 12 \end{pmatrix}
$$

$$
= \begin{pmatrix} 1 & 0 & 0 \\ 0 & 1 & 0 \\ 0 & 0 & 1 \end{pmatrix} \begin{pmatrix} -13/7 \\ -32/7 \\ 104/7 \end{pmatrix}.
$$

Now we wish to have a unity element in the third row and third column, and therefore we multiply the third row by the reciprocal of the third element in the third row (namely 7/52), obtaining

$$
\begin{pmatrix} 1 & 0 & -10/7 \\ 0 & 1 & -9/7 \\ 0 & 0 & 1 \end{pmatrix} \begin{pmatrix} x_1 \\ x_2 \\ x_3 \end{pmatrix} = \begin{pmatrix} 2/7 & 3/7 & 0 \\ -1/7 & 2/7 & 0 \\ -9/52 & -10/52 & 7/52 \end{pmatrix} \begin{pmatrix} 10 \\ -11 \\ 12 \end{pmatrix}
$$

$$
= \begin{pmatrix} 1 & 0 & 0 \\ 0 & 1 & 0 \\ 0 & 0 & 1 \end{pmatrix} \begin{pmatrix} -13/7 \\ -32/7 \\ 2 \end{pmatrix}.
$$

Now to obtain zeros for the other elements in the third column we multiply the third row by the negative of the third element in the second row and add to the second row; and then we multiply the third row by the negative of the third element in the first row and add to the first row, obtaining as a final result

$$
\begin{pmatrix} 1 & 0 & 0 \\ 0 & 1 & 0 \\ 0 & 0 & 1 \end{pmatrix} \begin{pmatrix} x_1 \\ x_2 \\ x_3 \end{pmatrix} = \begin{pmatrix} 2/52 & 8/52 & 10/52 \\ -19/52 & 2/52 & 9/52 \\ -9/52 & -10/52 & 7/52 \end{pmatrix} \begin{pmatrix} 10 \\ -11 \\ 12 \end{pmatrix}
$$

$$
= \begin{pmatrix} 1 & 0 & 0 \\ 0 & 1 & 0 \\ 0 & 0 & 1 \end{pmatrix} \begin{pmatrix} 1 \\ -2 \\ 2 \end{pmatrix}.
$$

Setting the first term in our double equality equal to the third, we obtain

$$
\begin{pmatrix} 1 & 0 & 0 \\ 0 & 1 & 0 \\ 0 & 0 & 1 \end{pmatrix} \begin{pmatrix} x_1 \\ x_2 \\ x_3 \end{pmatrix} = \begin{pmatrix} 1 & 0 & 0 \\ 0 & 1 & 0 \\ 0 & 0 & 1 \end{pmatrix} \begin{pmatrix} 1 \\ -2 \\ 2 \end{pmatrix}
$$

or using matrix multiplication with the identity matrix

$$\begin{pmatrix} x_1 \\ x_2 \\ x_3 \end{pmatrix} = \begin{pmatrix} 1 \\ -2 \\ 2 \end{pmatrix}.$$

But by the definition of the equality of two matrices, we obtain

$$x_1 = 1, \ x_2 = -2, \ x_3 = 2.$$

That this is the correct set of values can be verified by direct substitution in the original equations.

Turning to the second term in our double equality above, we find that it is the same as the third term after performing the matrix multiplication. But what meaning does it have? This is soon evident if we take the product of the original matrix of the coefficients and the third order matrix in our second term. We have

$$\begin{pmatrix} 2 & -3 & 1 \\ 1 & 2 & -4 \\ 4 & -1 & 3 \end{pmatrix} \begin{pmatrix} 2/52 & 8/52 & 10/52 \\ -19/52 & 2/52 & 9/52 \\ -9/52 & -10/52 & 7/52 \end{pmatrix} = \begin{pmatrix} 1 & 0 & 0 \\ 0 & 1 & 0 \\ 0 & 0 & 1 \end{pmatrix}.$$

Therefore, these matrices are inverses. This would indicate that if a series of elementary row operations will reduce a given matrix to the identity matrix, that the same series of elementary row operations applied to the identity matrix will change it to the inverse of the original matrix. This is a theorem which can be proved. We shall not do so here.

But let us look at our original equations in symbolic form. They could have been written as

$$AX = IB,$$

where A is the matrix of the coefficients, X is the matrix of the unknowns, I is the identity matrix and B is the matrix of the constant terms.

Suppose we take the matrix equation and multiply both sides by the inverse of A, assuming that there is one. We obtain

$$A^{-1}(AX) = A^{-1}(IB).$$

Applying the associative law and properties of the inverse and identity, we obtain

$$IX = A^{-1}B = IC,$$

where

$$X = C = A^{-1}B.$$

Symbolically, C is our solution, just as if we had had a single equation in one unknown, and in the form implied in the second term of our example.

But note that there would have been no solution if A had not had an inverse. This is consistent with Theorem 2 and its corollary. It is the same restriction that we have encountered before in the theory of groups. Recall that if a and b are members of a group then the equation $ax = b$ always has a unique solution. But this is because a must have an inverse a^{-1} in order to belong to a group, and then the solution is $x = a^{-1}b$.

The technique which we have used in solving the simultaneous equations above by matrix methods is called the Gauss-Jordan technique. It may be used for any number of equations, with the same number of unknowns, provided that there is a unique solution. It is well suited for use in programming for high speed computers, since the same operations are used over and over again. We shall demonstrate this later in-our work.

Exercises

1. Solve the following set of equations by the Gauss-Jordan process.

(a)
$$2x_1 + 3x_2 = 7$$
$$x_1 - 2x_2 = 5.$$

(b)
$$3x_1 + x_2 - x_3 = 2$$
$$4x_1 - x_2 + 2x_3 = 8$$
$$x_1 + 2x_2 + x_3 = 8.$$

(c)
$$2x_2 + x_3 = 2$$
$$x_1 + x_2 - x_3 = -4$$
$$3x_1 + x_2 = 2.$$

2. Find the inverse of the matrix of coefficients in each part of problem 1, using the Gauss-Jordan process.

3. Solve the following set of equations by the Gauss-Jordan process. Also find the inverse of the matrix of coefficients.

$$x_1 - x_2 + 2x_3 - x_4 = 3$$
$$2x_1 + 3x_2 - 4x_3 + x_4 = -8$$
$$2x_1 + 4x_2 + x_3 + x_4 = 0$$
$$x_1 - x_2 + 5x_3 + 3x_4 = 25.$$

4. Prove that the following set of equations have no solution, using the Gauss-Jordan process.
$$2x_1 + 2x_2 + x_3 + x_4 = 1$$
$$x_1 - x_2 + x_3 - x_4 = 3$$
$$3x_1 - 2x_2 + 2x_3 + 3x_4 = 2$$
$$7x_1 - 2x_2 + 5x_3 + 2x_4 = 5.$$

5. Show that the following set of equations have an infinite number of solutions by use of the Gauss-Jordan process.

$$x_1 + x_2 + x_3 = 2$$
$$x_1 - x_2 - x_3 = 1$$
$$5x_1 - x_2 - x_3 = 7.$$

6. Find the set of values of b for which there are unique solutions to the following set of equations. Then for each value of b for which there is no unique solution express the coefficients of the third equation as a linear combination of the first two equations.

$$x_1 + 2x_2 + 3x_3 = 1$$
$$3x_1 + x_2 + 4x_3 = -2$$
$$x_1 - 3x_2 + bx_3 = 5.$$

7. Write out a formal procedure for the Gauss-Jordan process for the ith row.

8. Derive the inverse matrix for

$$A = \begin{pmatrix} a_{11} & a_{12} \\ a_{21} & a_{22} \end{pmatrix}$$

by the Gauss-Jordan method, indicating any restrictions on the a_{ij} as you proceed.

3 | FORTRAN PROGRAMMING

1. Introduction

With the advent of the electronic computer the mathematician or engineer who wished to use one in his work was faced with the problem of converting his proposed computations into a language which the computer would recognize. At the same time, since it is not feasible to have every mathematician or engineer become proficient in the language of the machine, it became necessary for the manufacturers to find ways of bridging the gap between men and the machines.

This is a problem in translation, just as if the mathematician or engineer were confronted with a text in a language foreign to him. He needs either to acquire facility in the language or to find an intermediary, perhaps only a dictionary in some cases, in others a person to translate for him.

Accordingly, the manufacturers have applied themselves to this problem and have come up with automatic coding systems that are remarkably close to the familiar language of mathematics. IBM is one such manufacturer who has made possible and probable the direct use of computers by many who might otherwise never have considered them.

The IBM language is called Fortran and means formula translation. The simplest version of this language will be discussed in this text. Although the computer may not be used by those studying from this text, it is the conviction of the author that it is to the advantage of the student to become familiar with such a language.

First, it gives him a better idea of the scope and flexibility of a computer, what it will do as well as what it cannot do. Its limitations are as important as its capabilities. Second, and more important, it stresses the fact that a student must know his mathematics well before he can give his problem to the computer in proper language. Special cases and all restrictions must be carefully taken into account. It must be a logical program. The person with a superficial knowledge of his subject soon finds that he is not very successful at programming for a computer.

2. Statements and Operations

Just as in the description of any problem, Fortran consists of a series of statements of various types. The primary difference here is that they cannot be collected in a paragraph as I am doing, but must be set off individually on a line. As a matter of fact they cannot be too wordy. Counting every letter, character, number or blank they may take no more than 72 spaces. Any statement which takes more must be reconstructed into two or more statements, each with 72 or fewer spaces.

Since we may wish to refer to a particular statement somewhere in our program, statements are assigned numbers when this is to be the case. The number may be any integer up to and including 9999. There is no necessity, nor is it desirable, to give a statement a number, unless one wishes to refer to it, although it is correct to do so. Statement numbers need not follow a numerical order.

If a statement is to have no part in the computation but would be helpful in identifying the program, it is preceded by the capital letter C, with at least two blank spaces following the C. The computer will ignore this statement, treating it as a comment.

In order to give examples of Fortran statements, we first remark that the following customary algebraic symbols are used in Fortran, namely; + for addition, − for subtraction, / for division, and ( ) for grouping terms. The symbol for multiplication is the asterisk *, and that for exponentiation is **, such as X**2 meaning x^2. The symbol for equality is =.

Variables and arbitrary constants are denoted by capital letters only. But, in order to have a larger variety of symbols, up to five letters or numbers may be used for a constant or variable, provided that the first is a letter. Examples would be SUM1, SUM23, PROD4, A2B, CUBIC, etc.

Now suppose that we wished to find the average of the squares of three numbers A, B and C. Our Fortran statement could be

$$AVSQU = ((A*A) + (B*B) + (C*C))/3.$$

The equation

$$y = ax^3 + bx^2 + cx + d$$

becomes in Fortran

$$Y = (A*X*X*X) + (B*X*X) + (C*X) + D$$

It could also be written as

$$Y = A*(X**3.) + B*(X**2.) + (C*X) + D$$

Note that a multiplication symbol must precede the parentheses, contrary to usual practice in algebra. It is not necessary to use parentheses as they are shown in these illustrations. The computer will perform the operations of exponentiation first, multiplication and division second, and addition and subtraction third, working from the inside out. If several consecutive multiplications and divisions are made, they will be done in order from left to right. For added clarity parentheses will often be used in this text, even though they are not necessary.

A third and recommended way for writing the statement would be

$$Y = X*(X*((A*X) + B) + C) + D$$

This would give the most rapid calculation as the least number of multiplications by X would be involved.

Generally the first space is reserved for the comment C, the next four spaces are reserved for statement numbers and the statement itself begins on space 7. This gives a more readable program and is more compatible with the cards used and various computers.

A major problem in any computation is keeping track of the decimal point. This is no less a problem in the computer. First, it is recognized that if all calculations and the results involve integers only, then the procedures are faster and simpler. In order to have a way whereby the computer can distinguish between such problems and those in which other than integers are used, the letters I, J, K, L, M, N are reserved for the first letter in any symbol representing an integer. We refer to these as fixed-point constants or variables. When a known fixed-point constant is used, no decimal point can be used following the last digit.

It is apparent that the only problem is in the case of division. The integer 7 divided by the integer 3 is not an integer. In such a case the computer truncates the result to the largest integer contained in the quotient. For example, if

$$I = 7/3$$

the value for I will be 2. As a matter of fact this can be most helpful in some computations.

However, a fixed-point number is restricted to a maximum of four digits. If a number greater than 9999 occurs, such as 11296, it becomes 1296, losing the higher order digits. 523684 becomes 3684.

A process for keeping track of decimal points is built into computers. It is a slower process but quite desirable. This is done by recognizing the fact that any number can be written in the form $0.a_1a_2 \cdots a_8$, with $a_1 \neq 0$, multiplied by some power of ten. Thus $286 = 0.286 \times 10^3$. $0.00437 = 0.437 \times 10^{-2}$. With this consistent notation it is relatively easy to keep track of the decimal point. In the Fortran only eight significant digits can be carried, since the last two must be reserved for the power of ten. And ten digits is the capacity of machines, such as the IBM 1620, which is the basic computer used here in the discussion of Fortran.

Numbers written in this form are called floating-point numbers and, if arbitrary constants or variables, they must be represented by one or more letters or numbers of which the first cannot be I, J, K, L, M or N. If they are known constants they must have a decimal point, but they do not need to be written with powers of ten. This is accomplished internally. For example, we have 3., 281., 0.026, 26000. or 26.E3, 0.009 or 9.E-3., the E being understood to mean power of ten. A sign is necessary only in case of negative powers.

A basic law of Fortran follows. You cannot mix fixed-point numbers and floating-point numbers in any statement. There are two exceptions. An exponent may be a fixed- or a floating-point number. In an equality, if the expression on the right is fixed-point, the symbol to which it is equal on the left may be floating-point and vice versa. Two illustrations follow, with the results as indicated.

$$A = 1 + 3 + 4$$

means that we will have as a value for A

$$A = 8.$$

In other words, it supplies the missing decimal point. For another example, if we have

$$I = 12.6 + 3.7 - 4.7 = 11.6$$

this will mean that

$$I = 11$$

In other words, it truncates the expression to the largest integer contained in the value of the right-hand side and then removes the decimal point.

One special note should be made in regard to the equal sign. First, every symbol used in a Fortran program is stored in a ten digit location in the memory of the computer. As soon as a symbol is used on the left-hand side of an equality in a statement, its value in the memory is replaced by the value of the right-hand side of the equality. This changes the meaning of equality from its ordinary use. For example, consider the two statements

$$A = 3.$$
$$A = A + 5.$$

The second statement could not occur in algebra, but here it means to replace A by its original value plus 5.. Thus the value of A is set at 3. in the first statement and then changed to 8. by the second. We shall see good use for this.

If we wanted to keep the original value of A in some other location we would write

$$A = 3.$$
$$B = A$$
$$A = A + 5.$$

This would set B = 3. and then change A to 8.. The second statement simply gives another name to A and stores it in a second location, as well as keeping A in its original location and as its original value.

3. Control Statements

A valuable property of the computer is its ability to determine whether a number is positive, negative or zero. There is a control statement associated with this that allows the next instruction to be located at any statement. For example, the statement

$$IF \ (A) \ 2, 5, 9$$

means that if the number A is negative, the next instruction is statement number 2; if A is zero, the next instruction is statement number 5; if A is positive, the next instruction is statement number 9.

Furthermore, the quantity in parentheses may be any expression. For example,

$$IF((B*B) - (4.*A*C)) \ 6, 22, 1$$

would be very useful in determining whether the roots of a quadratic were complex, real and equal or real and unequal and proceeding accordingly. Note the commas after the first two numbers only.

The expression may be either in fixed-point or floating-point, but not mixed.

Next we have a statement that is also so much like ordinary English that it is almost amusing to think of it as an instruction for a computer. It is called the "go to" statement. A simple example would be

$$GO \ TO \ 14$$

meaning the next instruction is found at statement number 14. Just as in the "if" statement, it allows transfer of instructions to any point in the program before or after this statement.

Now we are at the point where we can write a meaningful program. Suppose we ask a computer to divide a given positive integer, N, by all positive integers which are less than or equal to half its value and to determine how many of those integers exactly divide the given integer. We write when $N = 10$,

```
        J = 0
        N = 10
        I = 1
        A = N
    5   B = I
        IF(B-(A/2.)) 2, 2, 6
    2   QUOT = A/B
        MQUOT = QUOT
        QUOTM = MQUOT
        IF(QUOTM-QUOT) 4, 3, 4
    3   J = J + 1
    4   I = I + 1
        GO TO 5
    6   STOP
        END
```

The statement number 6 simply stops the computer, and restarting it will not cause any additional operations. The END statement is necessary in all Fortran programs and signifies the end of the program.

J is the counter and set at zero to begin the program. N is the number to be divided and I is the divisor. It is set at 1 to begin the program. We define A and B to be floating-point numbers equal to N and I, respectively, for purposes of division. Otherwise, division of two fixed-point numbers always gives an integer as the answer because of truncation. The next statement, an "if" statement, determines whether the divisor is "less than," "equal to" or "greater than" half of the number A. If "less than" or "equal to" we transfer to statement number 2. If B − (A/2.) is greater than zero control is transferred to the statement numbered 6 and all operations stop.

Statement 2 performs the division in floating-point. The next statement truncates it to the largest fixed-point integer, calling it MQUOT, but not changing the value of QUOT. The next supplies the decimal point, calling it QUOTM, now a floating-point number. Now if QUOT was an integer, then QUOTM should be the same integer, and the division was exact; otherwise, it was not exact.

Therefore, in the next step we test the difference between QUOTM and QUOT. If it is zero, we go to statement number 3 and increase our counter by 1. So at the end of the first calculation for which the division is exact, the counter J will have the value 1. If the difference is not zero, we do not wish to increase the counter, so we go to statement number 4 which increases I to the next integer. Then we go to statement number 5 which initiates a new calculation.

4. Input and Output Statements

Now the previous problem is logically sound and the computer will proceed quickly with the calculation, but unfortunately unless one has a way to read the location and value of J in the memory, the result will remain a secret.

Accordingly, we need a method of output of data from the memory. This can be done on cards, using the instruction PUNCH, or by typewriter, using the instruction PRINT. It is a matter of choice and convenience. Using the PRINT statement, we would precede the STOP statement number 6 in the previous problem by the following statement, with 6 as the statement number.

```
6 PRINT, J, N
  STOP
  END
```

Notice that a comma must follow PRINT and each piece of data which is to be printed, except the last. Any number of pieces of data may be printed in fixed- or floating-point or mixed. When there is a choice, the advantage in printing in fixed-point is that it prints just the integer with no decimal point and trailing zeros to take up the eight digits. It is much faster.

Now examining our program we find that it is not too flexible since it will do this particular problem and no other. The computer is of its greatest value when used in problems in which the data may be continually changed to obtain new results while the body of the program remains unchanged.

In order to do this, it is necessary to feed new data into the computer to do the same problems. This process may be accomplished in either a READ statement, which introduces the data on punched cards, or an ACCEPT statement, which allows the introduction of data directly from the typewriter.

Using the ACCEPT statement we could change the problem just given to the following.

```
C    NUMBER OF DIVISORS OF AN INTEGER
1 ACCEPT, A, B
  J = 0
5 IF (B − (A/2.)) 2, 2, 6
2 QUOT = A/B
  MQUOT = QUOT
  QUOTM = MQUOT
  IF (QUOTM − QUOT) 4, 3, 4
3 J = J + 1
4 B = B + 1.
  GO TO 5
6 PRINT, J, A
  GO TO 1
  END
```

Now the program is designed to return to the ACCEPT statement as soon as the computation for the previous problem is finished and the STOP is no longer required. For the inquiring reader, the data was read in floating-point to shorten the program. It could just as well have been done in fixed-point, with the same statements as before.

There may be as many different ACCEPT, READ, PRINT and PUNCH statements as desired anywhere in the program and in any mixture.

Now let us turn to the previous program and trace the actual operations and computation for a specific set of data.

We select $A = 10$ as the given integer, by which we shall divide all integers equal to or less than half of its value; at the same time keeping track of the number of those which divide 10 exactly. Although we know that 10 is divisible by 1, let us set $B = 1$ just to give one more check on the method. Since 1, 2 and 5 are the only integers equal to or less than one-half of 10, that divide 10 exactly, our final result should indicate three divisors.

On the typewriter we enter the number 10. first, with the decimal point since it is floating point, and the number 1. next, also with a decimal point. Whenever the program calls for A the number 10. will be used, and whenever the program calls for B the number 1. will be used, until either A or B is changed by the program.

Next the counter J will be set at 0 and stored as such—a fixed-point number—with no decimal point.

The computer will divide A by 2., obtaining 5., and subtract this from B, obtaining −4. . Since this is less than 0., the next instruction is found in statement number 2 . The computer then divides A by B, obtaining 10., and stores it in the location designated by QUOT. Then QUOT is changed to fixed-point with a value of 10 and stored in the location of MQUOT. Then MQUOT is changed to floating-point with a value of 10. and this is stored in the location of QUOTM. The difference of

QUOTM — QUOT is found to be 0. and the next instruction is found at statement number 3 . This increases J by 1 so that the new value is 1, in fixed-point, indicating one divisor has been found. Then B is increased by 1., changing its value to 2. . The next instruction is found in statement 5 which causes A to be divided by 2., obtaining 5., and this is subtracted from B, obtaining —3. . Since —3. is less than 0., the next instruction is statement 2 which causes A to be divided by B, obtaining 5. and stored as QUOT. This is changed to fixed-point, or 5, and stored as MQUOT. This is changed to floating-point, or 5., and stored as QUOTM. Then the difference QUOTM — QUOT is found to be 0. .

The next instruction is found, therefore, at statement 3 which increases J by 1 again, making it 2 . Then B is increased by 1., making 3. the new value of B. Going to statement 5, A is divided by 2., obtaining 5. and this is subtracted from B, which is 3., giving —2. . Since this is negative, A is divided by B, obtaining 3.3333333 and stored as QUOT. Then QUOT is changed to fixed-point, or 3, and stored as MQUOT. Then MQUOT is changed to floating-point, or 3., and stored as QUOTM. Next QUOTM — QUOT is found to be —0.33333330 . Since this is less than zero, the next instruction is found at statement 4 and B is increased by 1., taking on the new value of 4. . Note that J was not increased by 1 since the last value of B, namely 3., was not a divisor of A.

Tracing the remainder of this program is left to the student.

In general when one traces a program, as we have done above, it is convenient to keep a table of the values of each variable. This shows the present value and how it has changed. We illustrate for the preceding discussion. A—indicates no value has been assigned as yet. A blank space indicates no change has been made in the value of the variable.

A	B	J	QUOT	MQUOT	QUOTM
10.000000	– –	– –	– – – –	– – – – –	– – – – –
	1.0000000	– –	– – – –	– – – – –	– – – – –
		0	– – – –	– – – – –	– – – – –
			10.000000	– – – – –	– – – – –
				10	– – – – –
					10.000000
		1			
	2.0000000				
			5.0000000		
				5	
					5.0000000
		2			
	3.0000000				
			3.3333333		
				3	
					3.0000000
	4.0000000				

As the student traces the remainder of the program he should complete the table above, obtaining a final answer for J of 3 .

Exercises

1. Write a program for computing the value of any cubic

$$y = ax^3 + bx^2 + cx + d$$

for equally spaced intervals of arbitrary length up to some maximum x from a given minimum value of x.

2. Write a program to determine whether a given positive integer is exactly divisible by some given smaller positive integer or not.

3. Write a program to determine the average value of an arbitrary set of n consecutive positive integers; and arbitrary set of n consecutive odd positive integers.

4. Write a program to determine when $n!$ exceeds 9999, and also when it exceeds eight significant digits.

5. Write a program to determine the last term and sum of an arbitrary geometric progression, without using the formulas. Do the same for an arithmetic progression.

5. DO Statements

Frequently we may desire to perform a given operation a number of times, simply changing the data to be used. This is possible with various IF statements and GO TO statements in general. Another approach is the so-called DO LOOP or DO statement. It is written as follows, for example.

```
        S = 0.
        DO 6   J = 1, 4
        A = J
      6 S = S + (A*A)
        PRINT, S
```

This means to repeat the operation from the DO statement down to and including statement number 6 for each value of the index J. When J has reached its maximum value of 4 the program proceeds to the next statement below 6 . The sequence above would be as follows. J is set equal to 1 and then A becomes 1. . Then A^2 is added to the value of S, which was zero, making $S = 1.$. Then J is changed to 2 and A becomes 2. and A^2 is added to S, which was 1. and now will be 1. $+ 4. = 5.$. J is changed to 3 and A to 3. and A^2 is added to S, which was 5. and now will be 5. $+ 9. = 14.$. Then J is changed to 4 and A to 4. and A^2 is added to S making it 14. $+ 16. = 30.$. Now since J has reached its maximum, the program proceeds to the next statement which will print S as 30. .

Some comments follow. J can vary from any positive fixed-point constant or variable to any other fixed-point constant or variable in steps of one. If it is desired to increase J in steps of, say, 3 one would write

$$\text{DO 8} \quad J = 1, 28, 3$$

the last number denoting the amount of increase each time. When steps of one are used the third digit is unnecessary. In general we write

$$DO \; N \quad J = I, K, L$$

where I, K and L are all positive fixed-point constants or variables, and N is a statement number.

There are two basic restrictions in a DO LOOP. First, the index J cannot be changed inside of the DO LOOP. Second, the DO LOOP cannot end with an IF or GO TO statement. If one wishes a control statement such as IF or GO TO as a last statement in the loop, he follows it with a CONTINUE statement. When the program reaches such a statement it simply returns to the DO statement and changes the index, if it has not already reached its maximum. For example,

```
  DO 7   KK = 1, N
  IF (L − (2*KK)) 7, 8, 7
7 CONTINUE
  GO TO 6
8 LSQAV = (L*L)/2
  PRINT, L, LSQAV
```

This program not only takes us out of the DO LOOP if L should equal 2KK, but in such a case that value of KK will remain available for computation purposes. But if the DO LOOP is satisfied, the value of KK is no longer available until reset to some value.

There may be DO LOOPS inside of DO LOOPS, but one DO LOOP cannot start inside of another and finish outside. Any number of DO LOOPS may finish at the same statement.

Exercises

1. Write the program in Section 4 of this chapter, using DO LOOPS to the greatest extent possible.

2. Write the program for Exercise 4 in Section 4, using DO LOOPS where possible.

3. Use DO LOOPS, and write a program to determine which pairs of integers, each less than N, have a sum which is divisible by 3.

4. Use DO LOOPS, and find the multiplicative inverses of the integers modulo p, where p is a prime.

5. Write a program to determine the sum of the reciprocals of the first n positive integers; to find the sum of the squares of the reciprocals of the first n integers. Compare the latter sum with the value of $\pi^2/6$ as n increases.

6. If $\pi/4$ can be approximated by the expression

$$\left(1 - \frac{1}{3} + \frac{1}{5} - \frac{1}{7} + \cdots + \frac{(-1)^{n+1}}{2n - 1}\right)$$

write a program to determine an approximate value of π for a given value of n, and compare it with the exact value to eight significant digits.

6. Subscripted Variables and Dimensions

In some problems it is desirable to have an orderly notation for certain variables, rather than selecting letters at random. For example, in solving equations we used single and double subscripts to refer to the coefficients, variables and constant terms. In the same way in Fortran we wish to use this notation. But instead of writing a_{13} we write A(1, 3), and instead of i_2 we write I(2). We may even write A(I + 2, J − 3), provided that each subscript is positive. Each subscript must be a positive fixed-point constant or variable. If it is a sum, the first term may be a variable, but the second must be a constant; and the sum cannot be zero.

Furthermore, to reserve spaces in the memory, the maximum number of spaces that may be needed for a subscripted variable, floating or fixed, must be known in advance and listed in the program as a DIMENSION statement. For example,

DIMENSION A(3, 3), B(4), I(7)

will reserve 9 spaces for the A's, 4 spaces for the B's and 7 spaces for the I's. This statement must precede the first use of any of the subscripted variables.

Reading in the coefficients in a set of equations is quite convenient using a DO LOOP and subscripted variables. We might have the program

```
DIMENSION A(4, 4), B(4)
ACCEPT, N
DO 2   I = 1, N
DO 2   J = 1, N
2 READ, A(I, J)
DO 3  I = 1, N
3 READ, B(I)
```

This would read in the coefficients in the order punched on cards as A(1, 1), A(1, 2), A(1, 3), . . . , A(1, N), A(2, 1), A(2, 2), . . . , A(N, N), B(1), B(2), B(3), . . . , B(N). Then any one of these values may be used at any time in the program.

For example, suppose that we wished to substitute values of the variables in a set of equations to check the solutions. We might have up to, say, 20 equations and 20 unknowns, such as

$$a_{11}x_1 + a_{12}x_2 + \cdots + a_{1n}x_n = b_1$$
$$a_{21}x_1 + a_{22}x_2 + \ldots + a_{2n}x_n = b_2$$
$$\cdots$$
$$a_{n1}x_1 + a_{n2}x_2 + \cdots + a_{nn}x_n = b_n$$
$$n \leq 20.$$

Our program could be as follows.

```
          DIMENSION A(20, 20), B(20), X(20), S(20), DIFF(20)
        1 ACCEPT, N
          DO 2  I = 1, N
          DO 3  J = 1, N
        3 READ, A(I, J)
        2 READ, B(I)
          DO 4  I = 1, N
        4 READ, X(I)
          DO 5  I = 1, N
          S(I) = 0.
          DO 7  J = 1, N
        7 S(I) = S(I) + (A(I, J)*X(J))
          DIFF(I) = B(I) − S(I)
        5 PRINT, B(I), S(I), DIFF(I)
          GO TO 1
          END
```

Notice that S(I) must have an initial value of zero to take care of the first case when J = 1. After that we add the value of the previous term in the equation. Note also that it must be outside of the J DO LOOP.

7. Functions

It would be very convenient in many programs to be able to have some built in subroutines for calculating a logarithm or cosine or some such value, without the necessity for writing a special program for it each time in the body of the main program. A number of such commonly used subroutines have been made available and are automatically included in any Fortran program translated by the computer.

The most common ones are

> ABS(X) meaning absolute value of X
> SIN(X) meaning sine of X
> COS(X) meaning cosine of X
> ATN(X) meaning inverse tangent of X
> LOG(X) meaning the logarithm to the base e of X
> EXP(X) meaning the exponential of X with base e
> SQR(X) meaning the square root of X.

These all have floating-point values and X must be a floating-point constant, variable or expression.

For example, if we were solving a quadratic whose discriminant was negative, and we still wished to take the square root of the absolute value to write the complex roots, we would have

$$R = SQR(ABS((B*B) − (4.*A*C)))$$

It is also possible to have a floating-point subscripted variable in our function such as

$$Y(I) = SIN(X(I))$$

8. Miscellaneous

Although not necessary, there are a few variations of programming available on the IBM 1620 which are quite helpful. For example, there are three switches on the control panel called sense switches, and they may be incorporated into the program as follows.

IF (SENSE SWITCH 2) 5, 11

means if sense switch 2 is on, then the next instruction is at statement number 5, and if the switch is off, then the next instruction is at statement number 11 . The advantage of this control statement is that it allows the operator to control the program in part while it is running. Any of the sense switches may be used.

Finally, there is the computed GO TO as follows.

GO TO (6, 8, 4, 3), I

This means that if at this point in the program the fixed-point variable I has the value 1, then the next statement is that numbered 6, if $I = 2$, the next statement is 8, if $I = 3$, the next statement is 4, if $I = 4$, the next statement is numbered 3 . This GO TO is not limited to four possibilities, but may have any number.

9. Sample Program

Now one of the primary problems discussed in this text will be illustrated in Fortran language, with appropriate remarks. The purpose is to indicate how the computer can speed up the work, far beyond a man's capabilities, of course. But, in addition, the student should note the basic knowledge of the problem which one must have before the computer can be used.

The final point, to repeat, is a realization of the giant strides that have been made in easing the communication between men and computers. The success of IBM in the introduction of Fortran is a prime example of this. Its similarity to the familiar terminology of algebra is ample evidence of the success such companies have had in making the computer more readily available on a practical basis to the student who is unfamiliar with the electronics of a computer and its machine language.

We illustrate the Gauss-Jordan technique for solving simultaneous equations. Our basic procedure is as follows.

Read in N for *n* and the coefficients A(I, J) and the constant terms B(I). Store a duplicate set of the coefficients and constants for purposes of computation, in order that the original values will be available for a check when the solution is obtained.

Set a counter I = 1 to represent the number of a row.

Test the first diagonal element C(I, I) to see if it is zero. If so, print 9., 9., 9. and go back to READ for a new problem. It is left as an exercise to insert the instruction to interchange two rows.

If not, let R be C(I, I) and divide each element C(I, J) in the first row by R, and also divide the constant D(I) by R. This gives us a unity element in position C(I, I).

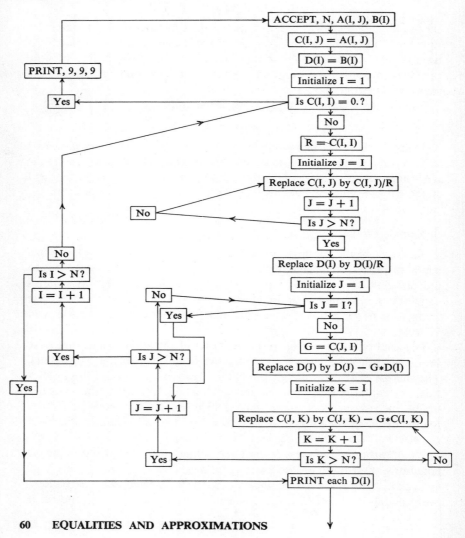

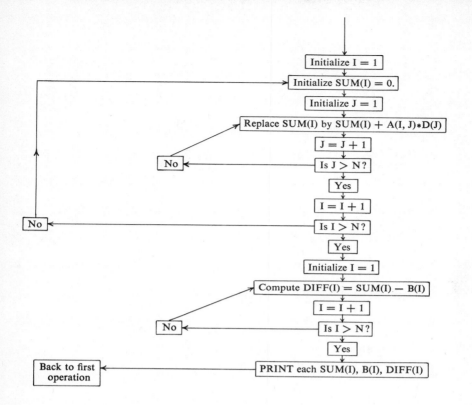

Then in all other rows, J, let G be the element C(J, I), where $J \neq I$, and replace each element C(J, K) in that row by itself less the product of G and the corresponding element in the Ith row, C(I, K) for all $I \leq K \leq N$, giving all zeros in the Ith column, except for the element C(I, I). Do the same for the constant term D(J) in the row J.

Replace I by $I + 1$ and repeat the process, until and including $I = N$. Then print each D(I) and these are the solutions.

Initialize a SUM (I) = 0. for $I = 1$ and replace SUM (I) by SUM (I) + A(I, J)*D(J) until J reaches N. Then replace I by $I + 1$ and repeat the process, continuing until I takes on the value N. This evaluates the left-hand side of each equation for the solution just obtained.

Compute the difference DIFF(I) = SUM(I) − B(I)

PRINT, SUM(I), B(I), DIFF(I)

In more compact form we write a so-called flow chart. This is very helpful in outlining the basic program, especially where there are loops and different possibilities after a calculation. It is also a good idea if someone else is to check your program.

The regular Fortran program is as follows:

```
C       GAUSS-JORDAN  PROCESS
   1 DIMENSION A(18, 18), B(18), C(18, 18), D(18), SUM(18), DIFF(18)
 100 READ, N
 101 DO 4  I = 1, N
 102 DO 2  J = 1, N
   2 READ, A(I, J)
   4 READ, B(I)
     DO 8  I = 1, N
     DO 6  J = 1, N
   6 C(I, J) = A(I, J)
   8 D(I) = B(I)
     DO 10  I = 1, N
 105 IF (C(I, I)) 14, 12, 14
  12 PRINT, 9., 9., 9.
     GO TO 100
  14 R = C(I, I)
 107 DO 16  J = I, N
  16 C(I, J) = C(I, J)/R
     D(I) = D(I)/R
     DO 18  J = 1, N
 106 IF (J − I) 20, 18, 20
  20 G = C(J, I)
     D(J) = D(J) − G*D(I)
 108 DO 22  K = I, N
     C(J, K) = C(J, K) − G*C(I, K)
  22 CONTINUE
  18 CONTINUE
  10 CONTINUE
     DO 24  I = 1, N
  24 PRINT, D(I)
     DO 26  I = 1, N
 109 SUM(I) = 0.0
 110 DO 26  J = 1, N
  26 SUM(I) = SUM(I) + A(I)*D(J)
     DO 28  I = 1, N
 111 DIFF(I) = SUM(I) − B(I)
  28 PRINT, SUM(I), B(I), DIFF(I)
     GO TO 100
     END
```

Statement C is simply a comment, with the letter C as a statement number specifying it as such.

Note in statement 1 that every subscripted variable must have a dimension assigned to it prior to its introduction in the program. The dimensions must be constants and in the case illustrated above are the maximum possible for this program on the IBM 1620 with a 2000 word memory. On a different computer the dimensions might be larger or smaller as a maximum.

Notice that statements 101, 102, 2 and 4 cause the coefficients to be read into the machine in order of the rows of the matrix of coefficients, with the constant term for that row following the coefficients. Therefore, the data cards must match this order.

In statement 105 we test to see whether the diagonal element $C(I, I)$ is zero or not. In this program we return to a new set of data, if it is. In a more general program we would then search for some other nonzero element below it in the Ith column, and interchange the corresponding rows to remove the zero element, if possible. If not, stop the process.

In 14 we let $R = C(I, I)$, so that in 16 we will not lose the original value of $C(I, I)$ when $J = I$.

In statement 107 J changes from I to N as the $C(I, J)$ for $J < I$ are already zero.

In 106 we do not want $J = I$ since we are using the Ith row as our basic row to obtain zeros in the Ith column. Therefore, we change all but the Ith row.

In 20 we let $G = C(J, I)$ for the same reason we let $R = C(I, I)$ above.

In 108 K varies from I to N for the same reason as above for J.

The three CONTINUES in 22, 18, 10 could be consolidated; they were inserted for greater clarity in reading the individual DO loops.

The D(I) in 24 is the solution for $X(I)$, of course.

In 109 the SUM(I) is initialized to give a starting definition and value for SUM(I) and must precede 110 or it will return to zero after every change in J, giving an incorrect result.

The DIFF(I) in 111 is theoretically zero, but it will not be in general because of truncation errors. This is one of the most serious problems in computer work. More general programs can help to reduce the problem, but it will still be present in most results to some degree.

Exercises

1. Modify the program in the preceding section for finding the solution of a set of simultaneous equations so as to interchange the necessary rows when $C(I, I) = 0$. Consult Section 5, Chapter 2.

2. Write a program for finding the subgroup of permutations generated by powers of $P = (123)$. See Section 6, Chapter 1.

3. Write a program for finding the multiplication table for the integers modulo N. See Section 4 of Chapter 1.

4. Write a program to find all the solutions in the set of integers, up to N, for the equation

$$2x + 3y = 5.$$

5. Write a program to find the product of two matrices of order 2; of order 3; of order n. See Section 1 of Chapter 2.

6. Write a program for finding the inverse of a matrix by the Gauss-Jordan method. See Section 5 of Chapter 2.

7. Write a program to determine the roots of a given quadratic equation, whether real or not.

8. Write a program to locate all of the real roots of any polynomial equation, up to and including the fifth degree, between successive integers. Assume that the roots are not too close together.

4 SETS WITH TWO OPERATIONS

1. Rings

Let us recall that up to now we have been considering the unique solution of an equation which involved only one operation, namely those of the type

$$AX = B,$$

whether the operation is matrix multiplication, ordinary multiplication or even addition, as in the type

$$A + X = B.$$

But suppose that there are two essential operations needed, such as in the type

$$AX + B = C.$$

We need a new definition and properties for a set of elements which may be combined by two operations.

Definition. A set of elements $a, b, c, \ldots$ forms a ring R under two operations, say multiplication and addition, (these are just the names of any two operations taken for convenience) if:

1. The set forms a commutative group under addition.
2. The set is closed under multiplication.
3. The associative law holds for multiplication; that is, $a(bc) = (ab)c$.
4. Both the left-hand and right-hand distributive laws hold; that is, $a(b + c) = ab + ac$ and $(b + c)a = ba + ca$.

Definition. If the ring obeys the commutative law under multiplication as well, it is called a commutative ring.

Definition. We denote the identity element under addition by the symbol for zero, namely 0. If there is an identity element under multiplication, and there need not be, it is usually called the unity element and is designated by the symbol 1. The inverse of an element b under addition is designated by $(-b)$. Thus
$$b + (-b) = 0.$$

Definition. $\qquad\qquad a - b = a + (-b).$

With the notation just given we can prove the various familiar laws of additive inverses for elements in a ring.

EXAMPLE. $(-a)(-b) = (a)(b)$. Consider

(1) $\qquad (-a)(-b) + (-a)b + (a)(b)$	Using closure and existence of additive inverses.
$= (-a)[(-b) + b] + (a)(b)$	Using associative law and left-hand distributive law.
$= (-a)(0) + (a)(b)$	Using property of an additive inverse.
$= 0 + (a)(b) = (a)(b).$	Using property of an additive identity.

Now from (1) we also have

$(-a)(-b) + [(-a) + (a)](b)$	Using associative law and right hand distributive law.
$= (-a)(-b) + (0)(b)$	Property of an additive inverse.
$= (-a)(-b) + 0 = (-a)(-b)$	Property of an additive identity.

Therefore,

$(a)(b) = (-a)(-b).$	Quantities equal to the same quantity are equal to one another.

In the above proof it is left to the student to prove that
$$(0)(b) = 0 \quad \text{for all } b.$$

On the other hand, in a ring the statement
$$(b)(c) = 0.$$
does not imply either $b = 0$ or $c = 0$.

Definition. If $b \neq 0$ and $c \neq 0$ and $(b)(c) = 0$, then b and c are called proper divisors of zero.

For example, the set of integers modulo 8 forms a ring. But in that set

$$(2)(4) = 0.$$

The numbers 2 and 4 are called proper divisors of zero. We recall the difficulty we had in this respect in determining which sets of nonzero integers modulo n form a group under multiplication. There was no such problem under addition.

Exercises

1. Prove that in a ring R

$$(0)(b) = (b)(0) = 0 \quad \text{for all } b \text{ in } R.$$

2. Prove

$$(-a)(b) = -(ab)$$

for all elements a, b in a ring.

3. Prove

$$a(b - c) = ab - ac$$
$$(b - c)a = ba - ca$$

for all elements a, b, c in a ring.

4. Find a ring in which there are proper divisors of zero. Show that in the ring

$$ac = ab$$

does not imply

$$c = b.$$

5. Prove that the set of all matrices

$$A = (a_{ij}) \qquad i = 1, 2 \quad j = 1, 2,$$

where a_{ij} is a real number, forms a ring under addition and multiplication. Is it a commutative ring? Does it have a unity element? Are there proper divisors of zero?

2. Examples of a Ring

One way to study whether or not the set of integers modulo 8 forms a ring is to construct both the addition and multiplication tables for the set as in Tables 9 and 10.

From the addition table we note that the set is closed under addition.

Since the set of all integers is associative under addition, the subset $\{0, 1, \ldots, 7\}$ is associative under addition.

0 is the identity element under addition.

Each element has its own additive inverse, since 0 appears once in every row and in every column.

The set is commutative under addition, since the table is symmetric with respect to the principal diagonal.

Therefore, the set is a commutative group under addition.

From the multiplication table we note that the set is closed under multiplication.

Since the set of all integers is associative under multiplication, the subset $\{0, 1, \ldots, 7\}$ is associative under multiplication.

Table 9

+	0	1	2	3	4	5	6	7
0	0	1	2	3	4	5	6	7
1	1	2	3	4	5	6	7	0
2	2	3	4	5	6	7	0	1
3	3	4	5	6	7	0	1	2
4	4	5	6	7	0	1	2	3
5	5	6	7	0	1	2	3	4
6	6	7	0	1	2	3	4	5
7	7	0	1	2	3	4	5	6

Table 10

×	0	1	2	3	4	5	6	7
0	0	0	0	0	0	0	0	0
1	0	1	2	3	4	5	6	7
2	0	2	4	6	0	2	4	6
3	0	3	6	1	4	7	2	5
4	0	4	0	4	0	4	0	4
5	0	5	2	7	4	1	6	3
6	0	6	4	2	0	6	4	2
7	0	7	6	5	4	3	2	1

Since the set of all integers satisfies the right- and left-hand distributive laws, the subset $\{0, 1, \ldots, 7\}$ satisfies them also.

The set is commutative under multiplication, since the table is symmetric with respect to the principal diagonal.

Therefore, the set is a commutative ring under addition and multiplication. Furthermore, it has a unity element 1.

It should be remarked that the order of selection of the operations is most important. Recall that we have seen previously that the operations by which members of a set are to be combined are as important as the members themselves.

For example, this set does not form a commutative group under multiplication. Although it is closed, the associative law holds, and there is an identity element under multiplication, not every element has a multiplicative inverse. 0 has no inverse, nor does 2, 4 or 6.

Furthermore, if we interchanged the operations of addition and multiplication, we find that the distributive laws do not hold. We would write

$$a + (bc) = (a + b)(a + c)$$

or for example, in the set $\{0, 1, \ldots, 7\}$,

$$2 + (3 \times 5) = (2 + 3)(2 + 5)$$

or $$1 = 3$$

which is false.

One might well ask whether there is any set of elements, with two operations, such that they could be interchanged and still have valid distributive laws. The answer is yes.

EXAMPLE. Consider the set S of all points within and on the circumference of a circle of radius 4 placed on a rectangular coordinate system with center at the origin. Let A be a subset of S, consisting of all points within and on the circumference of a circle of radius 3 with center at the origin. Let B and C be subsets of S, consisting of all points within and on the circumference of circles of radius 2 and 1, respectively, with centers at the origin.

Definition. We define

$$A \cap B$$

to mean those points which belong to subset A and also belong to subset B. We define

$$A \cup B$$

to mean those points which belong to subset A or belong to subset B or belong to both.

As distributive laws we write, taking $\cap$ as multiplication and $\cup$ as addition,

$$A \cap (B \cup C) = (A \cap B) \cup (A \cap C).$$

To prove this law, we suppose first that a point belongs to the set on the left-hand side of the equation. If it does, it belongs to A *and* to B or C or both. Now it must also belong to the set on the right-hand side of the equation if the equation is to be true. This means the point must belong to either $A \cap B$ or $A \cap C$ or both. But we know it belongs to A and either B or C or both; therefore, it belongs to $A \cap B$ or $A \cap C$ or both by definition.

Now we have to show that if the point belongs to the set on the right-hand side of the equation, it must belong to the set on the left. This will prove that the equality holds. The rest of the proof is left as an exercise.

Now we write, taking $\cup$ as multiplication and $\cap$ as addition,

$$A \cup (B \cap C) = (A \cup B) \cap (A \cup C).$$

This distributive law also holds. The proof is similar to the one above and is left for an exercise. Thus we have demonstrated a case where interchanging two operations does not destroy the distributive property.

The student should be fully aware that this does not mean that the element on the left side of the equation in the first case is the same as the element on the left side in the second case.

Exercises

1. Prove that the set of all integers forms a ring under addition and multiplication. What assumptions are necessary?

2. Find an example of a ring with no unity element.

3. Prove that the set of all integers modulo 5 forms a ring under addition and multiplication.

4. Do the numbers of the form $a + b\sqrt{3}$ form a ring under addition and multiplication, if a and b are integers; if a and b are integers modulo 3?

5. Prove the remainder of the theorem in the text on the validity of

$$A \cap (B \cup C) = (A \cap B) \cup (A \cap C).$$

6. Prove that the law

$$A \cup (B \cap C) = (A \cup B) \cap (A \cup C)$$

is valid for A, B, C defined as in the text.

7. Show that in general

$$A \cap (B \cup C) \neq A \cup (B \cap C).$$

3. Solutions of Equations in a Ring

Regardless of the nice definition and properties just developed, we have not answered our basic question. Can we solve an equation of the form

$$AX + B = C$$

where A, B and C are members of a ring R? Recall that we demand a unique solution which is a member of the set R. The answer is "not always."

Consider the equation

$$2x + 6 = 2$$

in the ring of integers modulo 8. This can be written as

$$(2x + 6) + (-2) = 2 + (-2),$$

since in a ring the additive inverse exists for each element, and the set is closed under addition.

$$\therefore \quad 2x + 4 = 0$$

using the associative law and properties of an inverse and identity under addition. Then we write

$$2(x + 2) = 0$$

using the left-hand distributive law. Now we are tempted to say that

either

$$2 = 0$$

or

$$x + 2 = 0.$$

Since

$$2 \neq 0,$$

this would imply that

$$x + 2 = 0.$$

But, although this is possible, it is not necessary, since

if

$$x + 2 = 4$$

then

$$2(x + 2) = 0,$$

since

$$(2)(4) = 0$$

in this ring. Therefore, although we can find a solution which belongs to the ring, it is not unique. The two possible solutions are

$$x = 2 \quad \text{and} \quad x = 6.$$

Exercises

1. Determine whether or not the following equation has a unique solution in the ring of integers. Use only legitimate operations.

$$3x + 5 = 11.$$

2. Determine whether or not the following equation has a unique solution in the ring of even integers. Use only legitimate operations.

$$2x + 6 = 12.$$

3. Determine whether or not the following equation has a unique solution in the set of integers modulo 5. Use only legitimate operations.

$$4x + 1 = 3.$$

4. Give three examples of an equation of the form

$$AX + B = C$$

in a ring R, such that the first has no solutions in R, the second a unique solution in R and the third more than one solution in R. In the first and third cases show the particular difficulty which prevents a unique solution.

5. Solve, if possible, the matrix equation

$$AX + B = C,$$

where

$$A = \begin{pmatrix} 2 & 1 \\ -1 & 3 \end{pmatrix}, \qquad B = \begin{pmatrix} 3 & 2 \\ 1 & 0 \end{pmatrix}, \qquad C = \begin{pmatrix} 1 & 4 \\ -2 & 3 \end{pmatrix}.$$

4. Integral Domains

In an attempt to overcome the difficulties inherent in solving the linear equation

$$AX + B = C$$

in a ring, because of the possibility of proper divisors of zero, we turn to a more restricted set of elements.

Definition. An integral domain is a commutative ring, with at least two elements, containing a unity element and no proper divisors of zero.

Since the ring of all integers under addition and multiplication is also commutative, has a unity element and no proper divisors of zero, it is also an integral domain. Note that the name is well chosen in this respect.

We remark that there can be integral domains with a finite number of elements. The integers modulo 5, under addition and multiplication, are a good example. A look at the multiplication table for the nonzero elements indicates the absence of proper divisors of zero. (See Table 11.) Since 5 is a prime number, this reaffirms our earlier remarks about the nonzero members of this set as a group under multiplication.

Table 11

×	1	2	3	4
1	1	2	3	4
2	2	4	1	3
3	3	1	4	2
4	4	3	2	1

The definition required at least two elements and we note that the set of integers modulo 2, namely 0, 1, is such an integral domain.

Now for the first time we introduce the concept of positive elements in a set.

Definition. A subset P of an integral domain D is said to be a set of positive elements of D if P is closed under addition and multiplication, and for each element b belonging to D one of the following holds: either

b belongs to P, or $(-b)$ belongs to P, or $b = 0$. Any integral domain containing such a subset is called ordered.

The set of all integers under addition and multiplication is such an ordered integral domain.

Exercises

1. Show that the ring of integers modulo 7 is an integral domain.
2. Prove that the ring of integers modulo n, where $n = rs$, with $1 < r < n$, $1 < s < n$, cannot be an integral domain.
3. Prove that the ring of integers modulo p, where p is prime, is an integral domain.
4. Does the set of all numbers of the form $a + b\sqrt{2}$, a and b integers, form an integral domain? Assume all necessary properties of integers.
5. Does the set of all numbers of the form $a + b\sqrt{2}$, a and b integers modulo 3, form an integral domain?
6. Prove that an ordered integral domain cannot consist of only a finite number of elements.

5. Solutions of Equations in an Integral Domain

We resume our study of the solution of equations with the following example. Consider the equation

$$2x + 1 = 2$$

in the integral domain of integers modulo 3. Adding the additive inverse of the unity element to both sides, we have

$$(2x + 1) + (-1) = 2 + (-1).$$

Since
$$(-1) = 2$$

we obtain, after using the associative law and properties of the inverse and identity,

$$2x = 1$$

and from the multiplication table we obtain a unique solution $x = 2$ in the integral domain.

This solution might imply that each equation of this form always has a unique solution in an integral domain. We assert once again, however, that one example is no proof, unless it is the only example.

Consider the same equation in the integral domain of all integers. By using the same procedure we write

$$(2x + 1) + (-1) = 2 + (-1),$$

where
$$(-1) = -1,$$

and, using the same laws as before, we obtain

$$2x = 1.$$

But there is no integer x such that

$$2x = 1,$$

and the equation has no solution in the set of integers. Since this is a counter example we can state that not all equations of the form

$$AX + B = C$$

in an integral domain have a unique solution in the integral domain.

At the risk of too much repetition, we do remark that the equation $2x = 1$ has a solution in the integral domain of rationals, which includes the integers. But we asked for a solution in the original set of integers.

Exercises

1. Solve the equation

$$3x + 4 = 2$$

in the integral domain of integers modulo 7.

2. Solve the equation in example 1 in the integral domain of integers modulo 5. Does it have a solution in the integral domain of all integers?

3. Solve the matrix equation

$$\begin{pmatrix} 2 & 1 \\ 1 & 0 \end{pmatrix} \begin{pmatrix} x \\ y \end{pmatrix} = \begin{pmatrix} 1 \\ 2 \end{pmatrix}$$

in the case where the elements of the matrices are integers modulo 3. Are the matrices in an integral domain?

4. Does the equation

$$2x + 2 = 8$$

have a unique solution in the ring of even integers? In the integral domain of all integers?

6. Fields

In the previous section we note that we obtained a solution for our equation in the case where the coefficient A of

$$AX + B = C$$

had a multiplicative inverse in the set. This was true, for $A \neq 0$, in the set of integers modulo 3 and in the set of rational numbers. It was not true in the set of all integers.

We place an additional restriction on our set of elements to remedy this defect.

Definition. A field is an integral domain in which each nonzero element has a multiplicative inverse.

As examples we have the integers modulo p, where p is a prime, and the set of all real numbers. (under addition and multiplication in both cases, of course).

We pause to emphasize a difficulty in notation. As long as our set of elements had but one operation, the notation for inverse or identity could be made easily, with no fear of contradictions. Now, with two operations, we find the need for an identity under each and an inverse under each. We have chosen 0 as our additive identity and $-a$ as our additive inverse for the element a.

Our multiplicative identity is, of course, the unity element and is denoted by 1.

Definition. We choose the symbol a^{-1} to denote our multiplicative inverse.

Both notations are consistent with that of the field of real numbers. Consider the field of integers modulo 5 under addition and multiplication.

Table 12

Element	Additive Inverse	Multiplicative Inverse
0	$(-0) = 0$	None
1	$(-1) = 4$	$1^{-1} = 1$
2	$(-2) = 3$	$2^{-1} = 3$
3	$(-3) = 2$	$3^{-1} = 2$
4	$(-4) = 1$	$4^{-1} = 4$

The set is composed of the elements 0, 1, 2, 3, 4. The additive identity is 0 and the multiplicative identity is 1. Table 12 should keep the student from treating the notation too carelessly as having the usual meanings in the set of real numbers.

Exercises

1. Prove that the set of all rational numbers is a field under addition and multiplication, assuming the integers belong to an integral domain.

2. Prove that the set of all complex numbers of the form $a + bi$, a and b any real numbers, and $i^2 = -1$, is a field under addition and multiplication, assuming the real numbers form a field under addition and multiplication.

3. Is the set of all numbers $a + b\sqrt{2}$, a and b integers, a field under addition and multiplication, where the integers form an integral domain?

4. Does the set of all numbers in example 3 form a field if a and b are integers modulo 3?

5. Show that the integers modulo 7 form a field and find the additive and multiplicative inverse for each element which has one.

6. Does the set of all matrices of order 2 form a field? An integral domain? Assume the operations are addition and multiplication and that the elements in each row of the matrices are real numbers. Then do the problem if they are integers. Then do the problem if they are integers modulo 3.

7. Why is the restriction "every nonzero element" present in the definition of a field?

7. Solutions of Equations in Fields

In this section we will not bother with a special case but turn directly to the most general equation. We consider

$$AX + B = C$$

where A, B and C are members of a field F and $A \neq 0$. A comment in regard to the last condition is left for the exercises.

Since every element has an additive inverse, we add $(-B)$ to both sides obtaining

$$(AX + B) + (-B) = C + (-B).$$

Then
$$AX + [B + (-B)] = C + (-B)$$

by the associative law. Then by the properties of an additive inverse and identity, we have

$$AX = C + (-B).$$

Now, since each nonzero element A has a multiplicative inverse, we multiply both sides by this inverse, obtaining

$$A^{-1}(AX) = A^{-1}[C + (-B)].$$
$$\therefore \quad (A^{-1}A)X = A^{-1}[C + (-B)] \quad \text{Associative law.}$$
$$X = A^{-1}[C + (-B)] \quad \text{Property of inverse and identity.}$$

Therefore, we have obtained a solution which is a member of the field, since the field is closed under multiplication and addition.

To prove the uniqueness, we assume another solution X'. Then we have

$$AX + B = C$$
and
$$AX' + B = C$$
$$\therefore \quad AX + B = AX' + B.$$

Adding the additive inverse of B to both sides and using the associative law, together with properties of an additive inverse and additive identity, one obtains

$$AX = AX'.$$

Multiplying both sides by A^{-1}, as before, and applying the associative law and properties of a multiplicative inverse and identity, we obtain

$$X = X',$$

which establishes the uniqueness of the solution.

It should be stated that the conditions established for a unique solution have been sufficient conditions only. They are not necessary, as the following case well illustrates. Consider the equation

$$2x + 8 = 4$$

in the ring of even integers under multiplication and addition. It has the unique solution $x = -2$ in the ring. However, this ring is not an integral domain, let alone a field.

Exercises

1. Give a reason for the condition $A \neq 0$ in the general equation

$$AX + B = C?$$

What can be said, if $A = 0$, about the number of solutions?

2. Solve the equation

$$5x + 3 = 8$$

in the field of rationals; in the field of integers modulo 11, both under addition and multiplication.

3. In a field if

$$X = A^{-1}[C + (-B)]$$

and

$$Y = A^{-1}C + A^{-1}(-B),$$

does

$$X = Y?$$

Why?

4. Find the conditions under which the equation

$$AX + B = CX + D$$

will have a unique solution in a field F if A, B, C and D belong to the field F.

5. Write a linear equation which has a solution in the field of complex numbers, but not in the field of real numbers.

6. Show that the following equation has a unique solution in the ring of even integers, the integral domain of all integers and the field of integers modulo 7, all under addition and multiplication.

$$2x + 6 = 2.$$

Does it have a unique solution in the ring of integers modulo 8 under these operations?

8. Fortran Programs

The work in this chapter affords an excellent opportunity to illustrate the use of Fortran, as well as review some of the basic foundations of the mathematics itself. For, as it has been said before, no program can be written successfully without a thorough knowledge of what one is trying to accomplish with each step of the program.

Consider the addition table for integers modulo n. Since the integers are commutative under addition, it is only necessary to find the entries on and below the principal diagonal, as the others can be filled in by use of symmetry. Refer to the tables for the integers modulo 8 in Section 2 of this chapter for an example.

However, if we wish to write a program to do this, how do we instruct the computer to determine only those entries on or below the diagonal and yet print out the entries above it as well? The following flow chart is suggested for addition of nonzero elements.

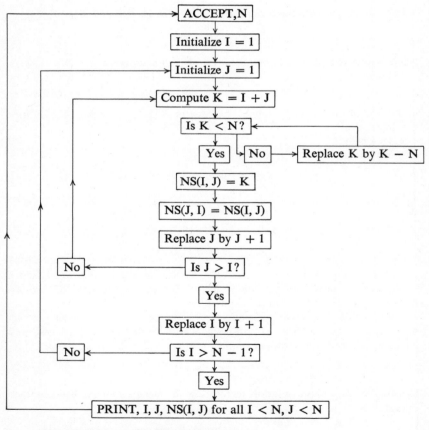

The Fortran program would be as follows for any N up to 31.

```
            DIMENSION NS(30, 30)
          1 ACCEPT, N
            L = N − 1
            DO 4   I = 1, L
            DO 4   J = 1, I
            K = I + J
         10 IF (K − N) 6, 8, 8
          8 K = K − N
            GO TO 10
          6 NS(I, J) = K
          4 NS(J, I) = NS(I, J)
            DO 12   I = 1, L
            DO 12   J = 1, L
         12 PRINT, I, J, NS(I, J)
            GO TO 1
            END
```

Notice in the first DO loop how J runs from 1 to I only, to save computation, and then statement 4 computes the symmetrical entry by equating it to the corresponding entry in the table. In statement 8 we subtract N from K if K exceeds N, and then test K again. We could have divided K by N and determined the remainder, but this would have been a more complicated program and K will never exceed or equal 2N. Therefore, at most one subtraction will be needed.

As a final remark on this program, it should be noted how the DO loop takes care of all of the testing of I and J values. This could have been done with IF statements instead. Such a program is left to the exercises.

We have discussed at some length the solutions of equations of the form

$$AX + B = C.$$

Consider a Fortran program which would determine all of the solutions if A, B and C belong to the set of integers modulo N.

One plan of attack would be to write the equation in the form

$$AX = C + (−B),$$

since every element B would have an additive inverse. Then one would test the products of all elements of the set of integers modulo N with A and compare the results with $C + (−B)$. All cases in which the equality held would yield a solution.

The following flow chart illustrates the procedures.

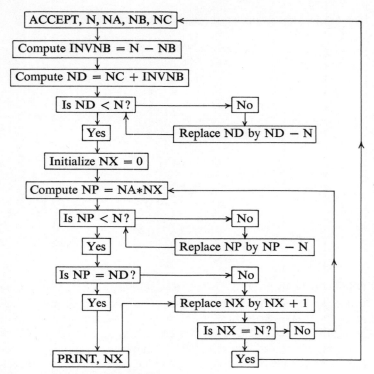

The Fortran program is as follows.

```
  1 ACCEPT, N, NA, NB, NC
    INVNB = N − NB
    ND = NC + INVNB
  4 IF (ND − N) 2, 3, 3
  3 ND = ND − N
    GO TO 4
  2 NX = 0
  9 NP = NA*NX
  7 IF (NP − N) 5, 6, 6
  6 NP = NP − N
    GO TO 7
  5 IF (NP − ND) 10, 8, 10
  8 PRINT, NX
 10 NX = NX + 1
    IF (NX − N) 9, 1, 1
    END
```

Fixed-point numbers have been used to speed up the computation. INVNB stands for the additive inverse of NB.

The approach in the program above was made with IF statements instead of DO loops. The student will find there is a great deal of flexibility in the way in which the programs may be written. There is really no one program for each problem.

Exercises

1. Modify the program given in this section for the addition table of integers modulo N to include the zero elements.

2. Write a program for the multiplication table of integers modulo N using DO loops wherever possible; using IF statements with no DO loops.

3. Write a program to determine the divisors of zero in the integers modulo N.

4. Write a program to determine the multiplicative inverses of the integers modulo N, whether N is prime or not, and which counts the total number of elements which have multiplicative inverses.

5. Modify the program given in this section for solutions of the equation

$$AX + B = C,$$

which restricts A, B and C to even integers, modulo N, and the solutions to even integers, modulo N. Do the same for odd integers.

5 | INEQUALITIES

1. Truncation Problems

In most work with computers, and in many cases involving hand calculations, numbers are restricted to a certain number of significant digits. In some problems this presents no major difficulties, but in others the solution may be materially affected as a result. (No distinction is made between the words "number" and "numeral" in this text.)

As an example, if the number 3840 is to be carried with only two significant digits, it becomes 3800. The number 0.00384 becomes 0.0038. Note that leading and trailing zeros are not affected for they may be taken care of by simply multiplying by an appropriate power of ten. Thus 3840 becomes 38×10^2, sometimes written 38E02 and 0.00384 becomes 0.38E-02.

Definition. To truncate a number means to reduce the number of significant digits in the number to some preassigned value, counting from the first nonzero digit on the left.

Note that this does not necessarily give the same value as rounding off the number. For example, both 3840 and 3870, truncated to two significant digits, become 3800; while 3840 rounds off to 3800 and 3870 rounds off to 3900. But the problems arising in either case are about the same, and we will discuss truncation simply by choice, and because it represents the type of approximation found in most digital computers.

Turning to the question of our algebraic laws, we find our first difficulty. We will show that

$$a + (b + c) \neq (a + b) + c$$

in general when truncation is used. For example, take the numbers 73, 33

82

and 69, and let us truncate to two significant digits. If we compute on the left-hand side first,

$$33 + 69 = 102$$

which truncates to 100. Then

$$73 + 100 = 173$$

which truncates to 170.

Now on the right-hand side we have

$$73 + 33 = 106$$

which truncates to 100. Then

$$100 + 69 = 169$$

which truncates to 160, and

$$170 \neq 160.$$

The true answer is 175 which truncates to 170. We note that associating the two numbers which give the smallest sum first gives an answer closer to the correct answer on its final truncation. However, try the numbers 84, 93 and 98 and this observation is shown to be false as a general principle.

The same problem occurs in multiplication when the associative law is used and no general rule can be given. We just have to face up to the inaccuracies which may result, and study our answers more carefully. Naturally, the more computations that are made, the greater the chance for substantial errors in the results.

This can best be pointed up by the Gauss-Jordan technique of solving simultaneous linear equations. We take the following example and assume that it is solved by a computer which truncates all results of any calculation to two significant digits as soon as the calculation is made.

(1)
$$3x_1 + 3x_2 = 7$$
$$3x_1 - 6x_2 = -11$$

which has an exact solution, $x_1 = \frac{1}{3}$ and $x_2 = 2$. Written in matrix form it becomes

(2)
$$\begin{pmatrix} 3. & 3. \\ 3. & -6. \end{pmatrix} \begin{pmatrix} x_1 \\ x_2 \end{pmatrix} = \begin{pmatrix} 7. \\ -11. \end{pmatrix}.$$

We multiply the first row by the reciprocal of 3., but the computer uses 0.33, of course, and we have

(2a)
$$\begin{pmatrix} 0.99 & 0.99 \\ 3. & -6. \end{pmatrix} \begin{pmatrix} x_1 \\ x_2 \end{pmatrix} = \begin{pmatrix} 2.3 \\ -11. \end{pmatrix};$$

then we multiply the first row by $-3.$ and add to the corresponding elements in the second row. (Note that the computer thinks that the first element in the first row is 1 and treats it accordingly.) We obtain

$$(2b) \qquad \begin{pmatrix} 0.99 & 0.99 \\ 0.10 & -8.9 \end{pmatrix} \begin{pmatrix} x_1 \\ x_2 \end{pmatrix} = \begin{pmatrix} 2.3 \\ -17.0 \end{pmatrix}.$$

We observe that the first element in the second row is not zero, as it should be, but the computer does not know this, so it proceeds to multiply the elements in the second row by the reciprocal of the second element, which is -0.11. We obtain

$$(2c) \qquad \begin{pmatrix} 0.99 & 0.99 \\ -0.011 & 0.97 \end{pmatrix} \begin{pmatrix} x_1 \\ x_2 \end{pmatrix} = \begin{pmatrix} 2.3 \\ 1.8 \end{pmatrix}.$$

Now the computer assumes that the second element in the second row is 1 and multiplies the second row by -0.99 and adds to the corresponding elements of the first row, obtaining

$$(3) \qquad \begin{pmatrix} 1.0 & 0.03 \\ -0.011 & 0.97 \end{pmatrix} \begin{pmatrix} x_1 \\ x_2 \end{pmatrix} = \begin{pmatrix} 0.60 \\ 1.8 \end{pmatrix}.$$

Theoretically, the first matrix on the left should be the identity matrix. The fact that it is not is due to truncation error. Now the answer should be $x_1 = 0.6$ and $x_2 = 1.8$. The computer does not know that they are incorrect, without checking, and the only recourse is to substitute them into the original equations, obtaining

$$3(0.60) + 3(1.8) = 7.2$$
$$3(0.60) - 6(1.8) = -8.2.$$

Then the differences between the original constants and those just obtained are

$$(4) \qquad\qquad 7. - 7.2 = -0.20$$

and

$$-11. - (-8.2) = -2.8.$$

Naturally, the ideal situation would be to have these differences both zero. The problem is to reduce these differences to zero.

Consider the general case for a moment. Suppose we have

$$a_{11}x_1 + a_{12}x_2 = b_1$$
$$a_{21}x_1 + a_{22}x_2 = b_2.$$

If

$$x_1 = x + t, \, x_2 = y + s$$
$$b_1 = b + w, \, b_2 = c + v,$$

then

$$a_{11}(x + t) + a_{12}(y + s) = b + w$$
$$a_{21}(x + t) + a_{22}(y + s) = c + v,$$

or
$$(a_{11}x + a_{12}y) + (a_{11}t + a_{12}s) = b + w$$
$$(a_{21}x + a_{22}y) + (a_{21}t + a_{22}s) = c + v.$$

Now we form one pair of equations by equating the first term on the left to the first term on the right in each equation, obtaining

$$a_{11}x + a_{12}y = b$$
$$a_{21}x + a_{22}y = c.$$

Then we form a second pair of equations by equating the second term on the left to the second term on the right in each equation, obtaining

$$a_{11}t + a_{12}s = w$$
$$a_{21}t + a_{22}s = v.$$

It is evident that combining the solutions of these two pairs of equations will yield solutions of the original pair of equations.

Accordingly, we form a new matrix equation with the same left-hand side as (2), except for the variables, and a right-hand side as the matrix of the differences in (4), obtaining

$$\begin{pmatrix} 3. & 3. \\ 3. & -6. \end{pmatrix} \begin{pmatrix} t \\ s \end{pmatrix} = \begin{pmatrix} -0.20 \\ -2.8 \end{pmatrix}.$$

We solve this matrix equation by the Gauss-Jordan method, and by letting the previous solutions be $x = 0.6$ and $y = 1.8$, we will add the values of t, s to the values of x, y, respectively, obtaining new solutions to our original equations (1).

However, the work is much easier, since the matrix on the left is identical to the matrix in (2), and therefore we will use the same elementary row operations as the first time. We do not bother writing the results on the left-hand side, since they repeat, but only those on the right-hand side. As successive steps we obtain

(2a)
$$\begin{pmatrix} \\ \end{pmatrix}\begin{pmatrix} \\ \end{pmatrix} = \begin{pmatrix} -0.066 \\ -2.8 \end{pmatrix}$$

(2b)
$$\begin{pmatrix} \\ \end{pmatrix}\begin{pmatrix} \\ \end{pmatrix} = \begin{pmatrix} -0.066 \\ -2.6 \end{pmatrix}$$

(2c)
$$\begin{pmatrix} \\ \end{pmatrix}\begin{pmatrix} \\ \end{pmatrix} = \begin{pmatrix} -0.066 \\ +0.28 \end{pmatrix}$$

(3)
$$\begin{pmatrix} \\ \end{pmatrix}\begin{pmatrix} \\ \end{pmatrix} = \begin{pmatrix} -0.33 \\ +0.28 \end{pmatrix}$$

$$\therefore \quad x_1 = x + t = 0.60 + (-0.33) = 0.27$$
$$x_2 = y + s = 1.8 + 0.28 = 2.0$$

after truncation, of course, in each case. Now substituting in (1) we obtain

(4)
$$3(0.27) + 3(2.0) = 6.8$$
$$3(0.27) - 6(2.0) = -11.$$

By checking these with the original right-hand sides in (1) we have

(5)
$$7. - 6.8 = 0.20$$
$$-11. - (-11.) = 0.$$

Now we would take the differences in (5) and write a new matrix equation

$$\begin{pmatrix} 3. & 3. \\ 3. & -6. \end{pmatrix} \begin{pmatrix} t \\ s \end{pmatrix} = \begin{pmatrix} -0.20 \\ 0. \end{pmatrix},$$

where $x = 0.27$ and $y = 2.0$ and solve again for t and s. Then combining with the previous x and y, we obtain a new pair of solutions x_1, x_2 for our original equations (1). We continue in the same way until the differences as found in (4) and (5), etc., are less than some preassigned tolerance. But we cannot hope for an exact answer because of the continuing truncation errors. If we demand too much accuracy, we may simply begin to repeat our values.

The point is that truncation errors are quite important. In examples such as this we may be able to compensate for them in part but not entirely. In some cases the errors may be too great to handle.

Exercises

1. Continue the solution of the problem in the text until the greatest difference between the original constants on the right-hand side of the equations and the constants obtained by substituting the derived solutions into the equations is equal to or less than 0.01, or the values of the derived solutions repeat an earlier set.

2. Compare $a + (b + c)$ and $(a + b) + c$ by truncating at each step to three significant digits and also by truncating only the final result. Use $a = 741$, $b = 352$, $c = 864$. Use $a = 446$, $b = 379$, $c = 828$.

3. Compare $a(bc)$ and $(ab)c$ in the same way as in problem 2, truncating to two significant digits. Use $a = 46$, $b = 32$, $c = 57$. Use $a = 24$, $b = 15$, $c = 38$.

4. (a) Using the symbol $T(A)$ to mean the truncated value of A to two significant digits, and given A and B as two digit numbers, find two conditions such that $T(A + B) = A + B$.

    (b) If A and B are three digit numbers, find two conditions such that $T(A + B) = T(A) + T(B)$; also that $T(A + B) = A + B$. (It is suggested that A and B be written as linear combinations of powers of 10.)

(c) If A and B are two digit numbers, find two conditions such that $T(AB) = AB$; also that $T(AB) = T(A)T(B)$.

2. Effect of Changes in Coefficients

In many problems the coefficients of the equations involved in its solution may be determined by experimental data. As such, their accuracy will depend upon many factors. Too often one finds the attitude that slight changes in such data will result in slight changes in the solutions. Unfortunately such is not always the case. Consider the following example.

Given the quadratic equation

$$x^2 + 9x + 20.3 = 0$$

one might feel that a truncation of the constant term to 20. would be quite reasonable, as it would only change its value by 0.3, and it would certainly facilitate the solution. We would have

$$x^2 + 9x + 20 = 0$$

which readily factors, giving $x = -5$ and $x = -4$ as solutions.

But suppose that we solve the original quadratic by the formula, and we obtain

$$x = \frac{-9 \pm \sqrt{0.2}\, i}{2}$$

as the solutions. Here the solutions are not even real values, let alone being close to -4 and -5. In a physical as well as a mathematical problem, this would make all the difference in the world in the final analysis of the results.

Take the problem of a set of simultaneous equations. For simplicity we consider the set

$$x + 2y = 3$$
$$x + 2.001y = 1.$$

Eliminating x we obtain $y = -2000$ and then, of course, $x = 4003$, for the set of values which satisfy this pair of equations.

But suppose that instead of the above set of equations our data was read such that we obtained

$$x + 2y = 3$$
$$x + 1.999y = 1.$$

However, there appears to be little difference from the preceding set as one coefficient has only been changed by 0.002. But we solve, again eliminating x, and obtain

$$y = 2000 \quad \text{and} \quad x = -3997.$$

We note that the change in the value of y was 4000 and the change in the value of x was 8000, and the signs are reversed as well. Yet the change in the coefficients was only 0.002. It should make one realize that any changes or approximations in values may have a tremendous impact upon the final results in any problem.

Exercises

1. Show that the pair of equations

$$x + 2y = 3$$
$$x + (2 + t)y = 1$$

and the pair

$$x + 2y = 3$$
$$x + (2 - t)y = 1$$

can have solutions that differ by any desired amount by proper selection of the constant $t \neq 0$.

2. Truncate the coefficients in the following equation to two significant digits, and determine the effect on the solutions.

$$x^2 + 30.6x + 203. = 0.$$

3. Truncate the coefficients in the following set of equations to two significant digits, and determine the effect on the solution.

$$342x - 548y = 20$$
$$349x - 541y = 183.$$

4. Find a quadratic equation such that a change of one unit in the constant term changes the solutions by at most 0.5.

3. Laws of Inequalities

Essentially, what we are discussing is the problem of approximations which is closely akin to the subject of inequalities. For every approximation gives us an inequality, in the field of real numbers, between the true value and the approximate value for an expression.

Therefore, we turn to a study of inequalities, both analytical and graphical.

Definition. Given two real numbers b and c, b is said to be less than c if there exists a positive real number d such that

$$b + d = c.$$

We also define b to be greater than c if there exists a positive real number d such that

$$b = c + d.$$

Note that this implies b is positive if and only if b is greater than zero.

The expression $b < c$ shall be read b is less than c, and the expression $b > c$ shall be read b is greater than c. Sometimes we use the expression $b \leq c$ to mean b is equal to or less than c, with a corresponding symbol for "equal to or greater than." It is permissible to write the expression $b \leq c$ also as $b \leqq c$.

What we are really saying here is that two real numbers are always related in exactly one of three possible ways. Given the real numbers b and c, either b is less than c, or b is equal to c or b is greater than c.

Since there are other ways in which two members b and c of a set of elements S can be related, we write the expression "$b \sim c$" to denote that "b is related to c" in some particular fashion. Note that this makes no sense unless, for a pair of elements given in a particular order, the expression $b \sim c$ is either true or false.

The symbol $<$ when used to relate a pair of real numbers has this property. In other words, either $b < c$ or it is not.

For examples of inequalities we have

$$2 < 5,$$

since there exists a positive number 3 such that

$$2 + 3 = 5.$$

also,
$$-1/4 > -1/3$$

since there exists a positive number 1/12 such that

$$-1/4 = -1/3 + 1/12.$$

Sometimes we have inequalities involving variable expressions such as

$$\sin x \leq 1 \quad \text{for all } x.$$

But also
$$-1 \leq \sin x \quad \text{for all } x.$$

Therefore, we can write

$$-1 \leq \sin x \leq 1 \quad \text{for all } x.$$

But what about operations with inequalities? Do they follow the same rules as those for equalities? For example

$$2 < 5.$$

Can we add 4 to both sides of the inequality? The answer is yes, since

$$2 + 4 < 5 + 4.$$

Can we multiply both sides by 4? The answer is yes, since

$$(4)(2) < (4)(5).$$

Can we multiply both sides by -4? The answer is no, since

$$(-4)(2) > (-4)(5)$$

because

$$-8 > -20$$

and

$$-8 = -20 + 12.$$

We see that we should proceed to prove some of the basic theorems relating to inequalities. It is sufficient to prove them for "less than" statements, since every such statement is also a "greater than" statement as well. The statement that 2 is less than 5 also means 5 is greater than 2.

Theorem 1. If b and c are real numbers and

$$b < c$$

then $$b + a < c + a$$

for all real numbers a.

PROOF.

$b + d = c$	For some $d > 0$, by definition.
$(b + d) + a = (c + a)$	Equals added to equals.
$b + (d + a) = (c + a)$	Associative law.
$b + (a + d) = (c + a)$	Commutative law.
$(b + a) + d = (c + a)$	Associative law.
$(b + a) < (c + a)$	By definition, since $d > 0$.

Theorem 2. If b and c are real numbers and

$$b < c,$$

then $$ab < ac$$

for all positive real numbers a.

PROOF.

$b + d = c$	For some $d > 0$, by definition.
$a(b + d) = ac$	Equals multiplied by equals.
$ab + ad = ac$	Left-hand distributive law.
$ad > 0,$	a and d are both positive, and positive numbers are closed under multiplication.
$\therefore \quad ab < ac$	By definition.

In a similar way we could have proved that if b and c are real numbers and $b < c$, then $ab > ac$ for all negative real numbers a.

In a study of inequalities the properties of absolute values often play an important role.

Definition. If b is a real number, then the absolute value of b is denoted by the symbol $|b|$ with the properties:

$$|b| = b \qquad \text{for } b \geq 0.$$
$$|b| = -b \qquad \text{for } b \leq 0.$$

For example,

$$|28| = 28, \quad |-32| = 32, \quad |0| = 0.$$

But what about the absolute value of a sum and a difference and a product? We prove the following theorem.

Theorem 3. If b and c are real numbers then

$$|b + c| \leq |b| + |c|.$$

PROOF. We consider the various cases.

Case I: $b \geq 0$ and $c \geq 0$.

$$\therefore \quad |b| = b$$

and

$$|c| = c.$$

But

$$b + c \geq 0$$

implies

$$|b + c| = b + c.$$

$$\therefore \quad |b + c| = b + c = |b| + |c|.$$

Case II: $b < 0$ and $c > 0$.

$$\therefore \quad |b| = -b$$

and

$$|c| = c.$$

1. If $b + c < 0$, then

$$|b + c| = -(b + c).$$

$$\therefore \quad |b + c| = -(b + c) < -b + c = |b| + |c|$$

since

$$(-b + c) - [-(b + c)] = 2c > 0.$$

$$\therefore \quad |b + c| < |b| + |c|.$$

2. If $b + c \geq 0$, then

$$|b + c| = b + c.$$

$$\therefore \quad |b + c| = b + c < -b + c = |b| + |c|$$

since
$$(-b + c) - (b + c) = -2b > 0.$$
$$\therefore \quad |b + c| < |b| + |c|.$$

The other cases are left to the reader.

In the same way we can prove that
$$|b + c| \geq |b| - |c|$$
and
$$|b| \, |c| = |bc|.$$

Exercises

1. Prove: If $a < b$ and $c < 0$, then $ca > cb$.
2. Prove: If $a > 0$ and $ab > ac$, then $b > c$.
3. Prove: If $a > b$ and $b > c$, then $a > c$.
4. Prove: $|b| - |c| \leq |b + c|$.
5. Prove: $|b| \, |c| = |bc|$.
6. Given a set S of elements $b, c, \ldots$ a relation $\sim$ on S is defined to be an equivalence relation on S if the following three conditions are satisfied:

    (a) $b \sim b$ for all b belonging to S.

    (b) If $b \sim c$ then $c \sim b$.

    (c) If $b \sim c$ and $c \sim d$, then $b \sim d$.

These properties are known in order as the reflexive, symmetric and transitive laws.

Which ones hold for the relation " $<$ " on the set of real numbers? Find some other relation on a set S which is an equivalence relation.

4. Solutions of Inequalities

Now we are prepared to solve certain inequalities. For example, given
$$2x < 3$$
the solution is found to be
$$x < 3/2$$
in the set of real numbers, after multiplying by the multiplicative inverse of 2, which is positive. But we note that there are an infinite number of values of x for which this inequality is true. Therefore, this linear inequality has an infinite number of solutions in the set of real numbers.

Naturally, the operation of multiplication is assumed.

The set continues to be important in the solutions of inequalities, just as it was in the solutions of equalities. For example, the preceding inequality would have one solution in the set of positive integers and no solutions in the set of positive, even integers.

Unless otherwise noted, we shall confine ourselves to solutions in the set of real numbers.

It is well to interpret the inequality geometrically, according to the dimensions of the space in which we are working.

Figure 1

In one dimension our solution is the set of points to the left of the point $x = 3/2$ as shown in Figure 1.

The darkened portion of the line represents these points. But the point $x = 3/2$ is not included.

In two dimensions our solution is the set of points to the left of the line $x = 3/2$ as shown in Figure 2. The cross-hatched area to the left of the line indicates the location of these points. But the points on the line $x = 3/2$ are not included. However, a solution must pair a value of x with a value of y to represent a point in two dimensions. We note that y may have any value, while x is restricted. Therefore, we should write our solution as

$$-\infty < x < 3/2$$
$$-\infty < y < \infty.$$

A particular solution is given by selecting an x and y to give us the number pair which represents our point.

We could consider the problem in three dimensions, and then our

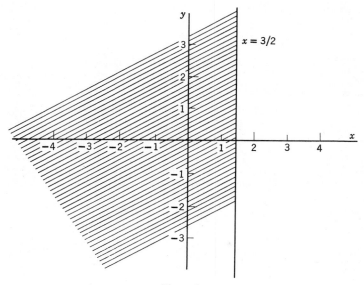

Figure 2

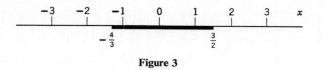

Figure 3

solution would be the set of points on one side of the plane $x < 3/2$, and the solutions could be represented as

$$-\infty < x < 3/2$$
$$-\infty < y < \infty$$
$$-\infty < z < \infty.$$

Of course, there is no restriction on the number of unknowns selected but only in the geometrical interpretation which may be used.

In the case of inequalities it may be possible to have a solution, or solutions, when there are more inequalities than unknowns. Consider the case in one dimension of

$$2x < 3$$

and
$$3x \geq -4.$$

Solving we have
$$x < 3/2$$

and
$$x \geq -4/3$$

or
$$-4/3 \leq x < 3/2.$$

Now all of the solutions may be represented by points in the finite line segment running from $-4/3$ to $3/2$ and including the point at $-4/3$ as indicated in Figure 3.

Of course we cannot always hope to solve, as illustrated by the following pair.

$$x < 4$$
$$x > 6.$$

It is impossible for a value of x to be both less than 4 and greater than 6 at the same time.

Now let us turn to an example in two dimensions. Take the set of inequalities

$$x + 2y > 4$$
$$x < 4$$
$$y < 2.$$

If we were to plot the lines represented by the equalities

$$x + 2y = 4$$
$$x = 4$$
$$y = 2,$$

we would have a sketch as shown in Figure 4.

From the inequalities we see that our answer should be points which lie above the line $x + 2y = 4$, to the left of the line $x = 4$ and below the line $y = 2$. This designates the set of points lying in the right triangle shown in the figure. No points on the perimeter are included. However, they would be included if an inequality such as $x < 4$ were changed to $x \leq 4$, for example.

By changing to inequalities of higher degree, the shape of the region in which our set of solutions is located may be changed to any desired pattern. Furthermore, if a geometric solution is given, the analytic solution may be determined, at least approximately, from the shape of the curves which form the boundary.

But what about a pair of inequalities in two variables, such as

(6) $$x + 2y < 8$$

(7) $$x - y < 2.$$

We cannot substitute values from one inequality to the other, as there is no rule for substituting unequals, of course.

What about adding or subtracting unequals to or from unequals? The answer is that this is valid for addition, provided that the inequalities are given in the same order. But remember that subtraction would amount

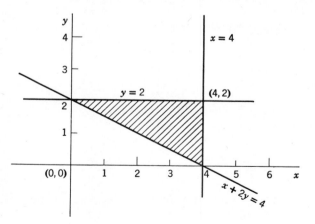

Figure 4

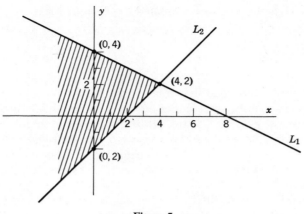

Figure 5

to multiplying both sides of the inequality by minus one, and this would reverse the order of the inequality.

Let us multiply the second inequality above by 2 and add to the first, obtaining

$$3x < 12.$$

$$\therefore \quad x < 4.$$

But it is impossible to solve for y in a similar fashion.

In equality (6) we could add $(-x)$ to both sides and then multiply both sides by $\frac{1}{2}$, obtaining

$$y < 4 - x/2.$$

Clearly y depends upon x.

In inequality (7) we could add $(-x)$ to both sides and then multiply by (-1), reversing the inequality and obtaining

$$y > x - 2.$$

Clearly again y depends upon x.

But since both of these inequalities must hold for any $x < 4$, we write

$$x - 2 < y < 4 - x/2, \quad x < 4.$$

For examples,

$$x = 3, \qquad 1 < y < \tfrac{5}{2}$$
$$x = 2, \qquad 0 < y < 3$$
$$x = -4, \quad -6 < y < 6.$$

It is evident that for each value of x there is an infinite set of values of y for which the inequalities hold.

Looking at a figure we see why this is so. In Figure 5, we have L_1 as the line obtained by changing the first inequality to an equality and L_2 as the line obtained by changing the second inequality to an equality. Our solution is the set of points which lie in the region located below L_1 and above L_2. Clearly, this region lies to the left of point (4, 2), and therefore the x values are always less than 4. But y may vary depending upon x. For example, when x is 0, y may have any value from -2 to $+4$, not inclusive.

A good question would be to consider the possibility of solving a set of simultaneous inequalities and having y bounded by a constant value, such as x was in the preceding problem. From Figure 5 it is evident that there are two such problems, one giving $y < 2$ and the other $y > 2$. A change of inequality signs in the original problem would be necessary. The question of which changes would give a desired result is left to the exercises.

As a final example, we may have a higher degree inequality in one unknown such as

$$x^3 - 2x^2 - 3x < 0.$$

We factor it as $\qquad x(x - 3)(x + 1) < 0.$

Now if the product of three factors is to be negative, we have the following cases.

$$\text{I} \quad (+)(+)(-) = -$$
$$\text{II} \quad (+)(-)(+) = -$$
$$\text{III} \quad (-)(+)(+) = -$$
$$\text{IV} \quad (-)(-)(-) = -$$

Case I says $\qquad x > 0, x - 3 > 0, x + 1 < 0$

or $\qquad x > 0, x > 3, x < -1,$

which is impossible.

Case II says $\qquad x > 0, x - 3 < 0, x + 1 > 0$

or $\qquad x > 0, x < 3, x > -1.$

$$\therefore \quad 0 < x < 3$$

for a solution.

Case III says $\qquad x < 0, x - 3 > 0, x + 1 > 0$

or $\qquad x < 0, x > 3, x > -1,$

which is impossible.

Case IV says $\qquad x < 0, x - 3 < 0, x + 1 < 0$

or $\qquad\qquad x < 0, x < 3, x < -1.$

$$\therefore \quad x < -1$$

for a solution.

We see that there are two different sets of solutions.

In a single inequality in one unknown it is sometimes desirable to find those values of the variable for which the equality would hold, and then determine between which pairs of these values the inequality holds by substituting convenient values of the variable.

Consider the previous example. We change the inequality to the equality

$$x^3 - 2x^2 - 3x = 0$$

or $\qquad\qquad x(x - 3)(x + 1) = 0.$

$$\therefore \quad x = 0, 3, -1.$$

We write them in order of increasing values, as $-1, 0, 3$.

Selecting $x = -2$, $x^3 - 2x^2 - 3x$ has a value of -10.

$$\therefore \quad x^3 - 2x^2 - 3x < 0$$

for $x < -1$. This is valid.

Selecting $x = -\frac{1}{2}$, $x^3 - 2x^2 - 3x$ has a value of $\frac{7}{8}$.

$$\therefore \quad x^3 - 2x^2 - 3x > 0$$

for $-1 < x < 0$. This is not the desired inequality.

Selecting $x = 1$, $x^3 - 2x^2 - 3x$ has a value of -4.

$$\therefore \quad x^3 - 2x^2 - 3x < 0$$

for $0 < x < 3$. This is valid.

Selecting $x = 4$, $x^3 - 2x^2 - 3x$ has a value of 20.

$$\therefore \quad x^3 - 2x^2 - 3x > 0$$

for $3 < x$. This is not the desired inequality.

Exercises

1. Solve the pair of inequalities

$$2x < 4 \quad \text{and} \quad 3x > -6.$$

(*a*) In one dimension numerically and graphically.
(*b*) In two dimensions numerically and graphically.

2. Given $\qquad\qquad 2x - 3y < -4$

$$3x + 4y < 11.$$

(*a*) Solve analytically and graphically.

(*b*) Reverse the inequalities and solve.

(*c*) Reverse the first inequality and solve.

3. Write the inequalities which define the line segment on the *x* axis between −3 and 4, including the first and not the second. Write a second degree inequality which has no solutions; one solution; an infinite number of solutions. Recall that $x \leq 5$ is called an inequality.

4. Write the inequalities which define the set of points outside of a circle with a radius of 1, with center at the origin, and inside of a square with sides of length 4, whose sides are parallel to the axes and whose diagonals intersect at the center of the circle. Do the same if one of the sides of the square makes a 45 degree angle with the *x* axis.

5. In problem 4 write the inequalities which define the set of points outside of the square in each case.

6. Find the set of values for which

$$x^4 - 2x^3 + x^2 - 2x > 0;$$

for which it is less than zero.

7. Find the set of values for which

$$x^2 - 2x - 2 < 0;$$

for which it is greater than zero.

5. A Trigonometric Inequality

Now let us turn to some inequalities in trigonometry, which we shall find most useful later in our work. We take a circle with a unit radius and an acute central angle *BOP* as shown in Figure 6. We shall call $\angle BOP$, θ.

Clearly from the figure the area of triangle *OAP* is less than the area of the sector of the circle *OBP* which, in turn, is less than the area of the right triangle *OCP* formed by constructing a tangent line *PC* to the circle at *P*.

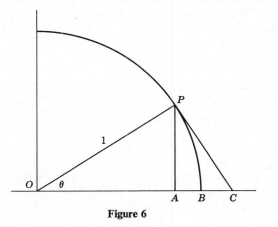

Figure 6

Since the radius of the circle is 1, by trigonometry

$$OA = \cos\theta,$$
$$AP = \sin\theta$$

and
$$PC = \tan\theta.$$

From this, the area of the triangle O

$$\tfrac{1}{2}\cos\theta\sin\theta.$$

The area of the sector of the circle is $\tfrac{1}{2}$ the square of the radius times the central angle expressed in radians, or (since the radius is 1)

$$\tfrac{1}{2}\theta.$$

The area of the right triangle OCP is

$$\tfrac{1}{2}\tan\theta.$$

$$\therefore \quad \tfrac{1}{2}\cos\theta\sin\theta < \tfrac{1}{2}\theta < \tfrac{1}{2}\tan\theta.$$

$$\therefore \quad \cos\theta\sin\theta < \theta < \frac{\sin\theta}{\cos\theta}.$$

As long as θ is a positive acute angle $\sin\theta$ is positive, and we may divide through the inequalities by $\sin\theta$ obtaining

$$\cos\theta < \frac{\theta}{\sin\theta} < \frac{\theta}{\cos\theta}.$$

This is a most interesting inequality relating a positive acute angle measured in radians with its sine and cosine. But now consider what happens in this inequality as θ approaches zero. Then $\cos\theta$ approaches 1 as does the reciprocal of $\cos\theta$. It is evident that the ratio of the angle θ to $\sin\theta$ approaches 1 as θ approaches 0. As a limiting case we write

$$\lim_{\theta\to0}\frac{\theta}{\sin\theta} = 1,$$

meaning that this ratio can be made arbitrarily close to 1 by selecting θ close enough to 0. As a matter of fact the error in evaluating $\theta/\sin\theta$ will never be any more than

$$\cos\theta - \frac{1}{\cos\theta}$$

since it must lie between these values. It is equally evident that

$$\lim_{\theta\to0}\frac{\sin\theta}{\theta} = 1.$$

What does this really mean? It states that an angle expressed in radians is nearly equal to the sine of that angle, when the angle is very small.

It means that the angle can be approximated by the sine of the angle for small angles, or vice versa.

Clearly all this is false when the angle is expressed in degrees as the derivation indicates.

But let us make a concrete comparison of $\sin \theta$ and θ for small angles. We find that for 2 degrees and 40 minutes, in radians, to four decimal places, $\theta = 0.0465$ and that also, to four decimal places, $\sin \theta = 0.0465$. Thus $\sin \theta$ may be replaced by θ with accuracy to four decimal places. Furthermore, this result is true for any angle θ such that $0 \leq \theta \leq 0.0465$.

This relationship should be one of the most effective ways of helping the student to understand the role of radians, and the notion of both the sine of an angle and the angle as numerical, dimensionless values.

Exercises

1. Prove: $\displaystyle\lim_{\theta \to 0} \frac{\sin \theta}{\theta} = 1$.

2. (a) Find $\displaystyle\lim_{\theta \to 0} \frac{\tan \theta}{\theta}$.

   (b) To four decimal places, for what set of values of θ can $\tan \theta$ replace θ?
3. Show that the use of degrees in the inequality cannot be valid.
4. By constructing another triangle in Figure 6, prove that $\theta > \sin \theta$.
5. Is $\theta/\sin \theta$ always closer to $\cos \theta$ or $1/\cos \theta$, or does the answer vary with θ?

6. Fortran Programs

In some problems it might not be desirable to carry out all calculations to the limit of the computer used. Suppose that we wished to truncate all results, as they occur, to three significant digits. Now, if the decimal point were after the third significant digit, then the number could be changed to a fixed-point number, which would give the desired truncation.

An example would be 263.84537, which would truncate to 263 when changed to a fixed-point number.

Since all numbers do not have a decimal point after the third significant digit, this simple procedure cannot be followed. However, if one could change the position of the decimal point to this position, truncate, and then change the decimal point back to the original position, the results would be as desired.

Take the number 48357.279, for example, multiply it by 0.01, changing it to 483.57279; then change it to fixed-point, obtaining 483; and then multiply by 100, obtaining 48300 as the desired result.

It is evident that one needs a program to determine the size of the number first, in order to locate the decimal point. Then it can be decided how many places the decimal point must be moved in order to perform the truncation. The following flow chart outlines the procedure. It is restricted to numbers equal to or greater than one.

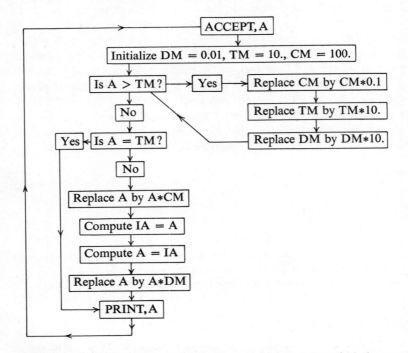

The role of TM is to determine between which powers of 10 the number A lies. The role of CM is to place the decimal point in A after the third significant digit, after the original position has been determined. The role of DM is to restore the decimal point to its original position after A has been truncated to three significant digits. The student should trace the program through with some specific numbers.

The Fortran program is shown on page 103.

Although we have illustrated the solution of some inequalities with exact results, this is no more possible in general than it is for the solution of equalities. Here the computer may play an important role.

In some cases of simultaneous inequalities we may be interested in solutions in which the values of the variables belong to the set of integers. In others we may be interested in points which lie within some prescribed distance from the curves which make up the boundary of the figure representing the inequalities.

```
        ACCEPT, A
        DM = 0.01
        TM = 10.
        CM = 100.
    8 IF (A − TM) 2, 4, 6
    2 A = AC∗M
        IA = A
        A = IA
        A = A∗DM
    4 PRINT, A
        GO TO 1
    6 CM = CM∗0.1
        TM = TM∗10.
        DM = DM∗10.
        GO TO 8
        END
```

We illustrate in the following example. Consider the inequalities

$$\frac{x}{4} + \frac{y}{12} > 1$$

$$x^4 + y^4 < 8^4 = 4096$$

$$y > 0.$$

See Figure 7.

(The curve is not a circle, although it has a similar appearance.)

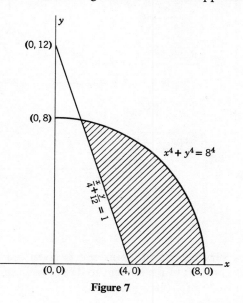

Figure 7

We shall write a program to determine the points which lie within the area and have integers as coordinates. This would give a kind of mesh which lies within the area.

We note that the restrictions on x and y would be

$$0 < x < 8, \quad 0 < y < 8.$$

This is evident both from the equations and figure.

The flow chart is as follows.

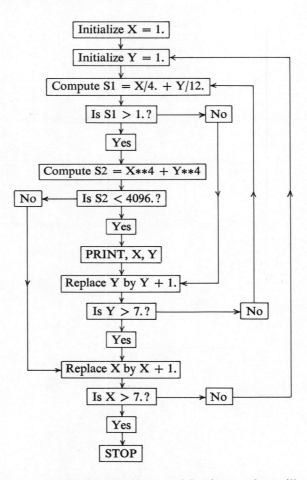

This is not a very flexible program and is given only to illustrate the technique. It will be left to the student to determine a program which will allow the mesh to be of arbitrary size.

104   EQUALITIES AND APPROXIMATIONS

The Fortran program follows.

```
      X = 1.
8     Y = 1.
1     S1 = X/4. + Y/12.
      IF (S1 − 1.) 2, 2, 3
3     S2 = X**4 + Y**4
9     IF (S2 − 4096.) 4, 5, 5
4     PRINT, X, Y
2     Y = Y + 1.
      IF (Y − 7.) 1, 1, 5
5     X = X + 1.
      IF (X − 7.) 8, 8, 6
6     STOP
      END
```

In this program why does statement 9 read 4, 5, 5 instead of 4, 4, 2? Note also that no ACCEPT statement is required. It is entirely self-contained.

Exercises

1. Extend the Gauss-Jordan program given in Chapter 3 so that it will remove as much of the error due to truncation as possible. See Section 1 of this chapter for procedure.

2. Modify the program in the preceding section for truncation of numbers to three significant digits to include numbers ≥ 0.01.

3. Modify the program in the preceding section for solution of inequalities to determine points whose coordinates are multiples of $\frac{1}{4}$.

4. Write a program to locate all points whose coordinates are multiples of $1/n$, where n is an arbitrary positive integer, which satisfy the following inequalities.

$$y < x + 20$$
$$2x > y - 25$$
$$x + 3y > -6$$
$$10x + y < 8.$$

5. Write a program to determine θ, both in radians and degrees, for which $\theta = \sin \theta$ to eight decimal places. Determine how closely $\tan \theta = \theta$ for the same θ. How close is $\theta/\sin \theta$ to $\cos \theta$ and $1/\cos \theta$? Also determine, within a given tolerance, for which values of θ we find $\theta/\sin \theta$ differing from $\cos \theta$ less than it differs from $1/\cos \theta$. (Use the appropriate subroutines.)

6 AREAS

1. Approximations by Rectangles

We now turn to an application of approximations and inequalities in the problems of finding the area bounded by certain curves. Although we shall solve certain specific problems, our technique will be a general one with wide application. In addition we shall demonstrate how an approximation may be used to find the exact answer in some problems.

Let us consider the problem of finding the area under the line $y = x$, above the x axis and extending from $x = 0$ to $x = b$, as shown in Figure 8. You may say that we already know the answer to this problem. But we solve the problem by a new technique, to illustrate the procedure and reassure the student by obtaining a known result. Then we shall extend the method to other problems, whose results may not be known to the student.

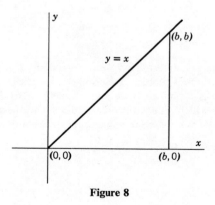

Figure 8

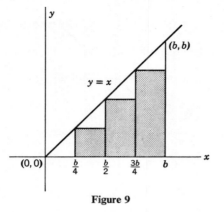

Figure 9

One of the basic shapes, for which we know the area, is the rectangle. We shall proceed to find the area of other shapes, using the rectangle as our basis of measurement. In Figure 8 let us divide the base into four equal segments and inscribe rectangles by erecting perpendiculars at the points of subdivision, rising up to the curve $y = x$, and then drawing horizontal lines to the right meeting the next perpendicular as in Figure 9. Actually there are four inscribed rectangles formed by this procedure, as the height of the first one is zero. The widths are all the same and equal to $b/4$. If we call A the actual area under the line, we obtain the inequality

$$A > \frac{b}{4}\left(0 + \frac{b}{4} + \frac{b}{2} + \frac{3b}{4}\right) = \frac{3b^2}{8}$$

where 0, $b/4$, $b/2$, $3b/4$ are the heights of the inscribed rectangles, since $y = x$ is the equation of the curve. Since

$$A = \frac{b^2}{2} = \frac{4b^2}{8} > \frac{3b^2}{8},$$

our results differ from the exact value by $b^2/8$.

Now we use the same subdivisions on the x axis and circumscribe rectangles by erecting perpendiculars at the points of subdivision, rising up to the curve $y = x$ and then drawing horizontal lines to the left, meeting the next perpendicular as in Figure 10. Adding the areas of these four circumscribed rectangles, all of width $b/4$, we obtain the following inequality.

$$A < \left(\frac{b}{4}\right)\left(\frac{b}{4} + \frac{b}{2} + \frac{3b}{4} + b\right) = \frac{5b^2}{8}$$

where $b/4$, $b/2$, $3b/4$, b are the heights of the circumscribed rectangles.

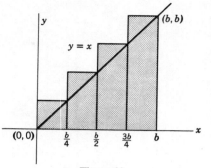

Figure 10

Since

$$A = \frac{b^2}{2} < \frac{5b^2}{8},$$

clearly

$$\frac{3b^2}{8} < A < \frac{5b^2}{8}.$$

It is apparent that by increasing the number of the subdivisions we can increase the sum of the areas of the inscribed rectangles, without ever exceeding the actual area. Thus we should approach the correct answer. In the same way we can decrease the sum of the areas of the circumscribed rectangles, without ever falling below the actual answer. As the difference between these two sums becomes smaller, the error resulting from the use of either sum, as the exact area, will become smaller.

But let us actually set this up in general analytically. We divide the interval from $x = 0$ to $x = b$ into n equal subdivisions. Let us call the width of each subdivision h and we have

$$h = \frac{(b - 0)}{n}.$$

Now, to obtain an orderly notation for the x coordinates of each endpoint of a subdivision, we letter as follows.

$$x_0 = 0, \; x_1 = \frac{b}{n}, \; x_2 = \frac{2b}{n}, \; x_3 = \frac{3b}{n}, \; \ldots,$$

$$x_{n-1} = \frac{(n - 1)b}{n}, \; x_n = \frac{nb}{n} = b.$$

Note that our last coordinate checks, as $x_n = b$, which it must.

In Figure 11 both the inscribed and circumscribed rectangles are shown, although the space indicates an arbitrary number of them, depending upon the value of n. Since the equation of the curve is $y = x$, the y coordinate for some point x_i is $y_i = x_i$. Therefore, using inscribed rectangles, we can write the inequality

$$A > h(y_0 + y_1 + y_2 + y_3 + \cdots + y_{n-1}),$$

or
$$A > \frac{b}{n}(x_0 + x_1 + x_2 + x_3 + \cdots + x_{n-1})$$

or
$$A > \frac{b}{n}\left[0 + \frac{b}{n} + \frac{2b}{n} + \frac{3b}{n} + \cdots + \frac{(n-1)b}{n}\right].$$

Or using the commutative law and the left-hand distributive law we find

$$A > \frac{b^2}{n^2}[1 + 2 + 3 + \cdots + (n-1)].$$

But the sum in parentheses is an arithmetic progression and this can be written as a single term giving us

$$A > \frac{b^2}{n^2}\left[\frac{(n-1)}{2}\right]n = \left(\frac{b^2}{2}\right)\left(1 - \frac{1}{n}\right) = \frac{b^2}{2} - \frac{b^2}{2n}.$$

Therefore, we have obtained a set of **lower bounds** for the area, taking $n = 1, 2, 3, \ldots$. This is a set of increasing values as n increases, approaching a maximum of $b^2/2$.

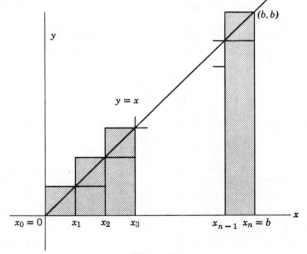

Figure 11

Forgetting, for the moment, that we know that the exact answer is $b^2/2$, we have proved that the answer is no less than $b^2/2$. We call $b^2/2$ the **greatest lower bound** of this set of lower bounds. Now we can write

$$A \geq \frac{b^2}{2}.$$

Now using circumscribed rectangles, we can write the inequality

$$A < h(y_1 + y_2 + y_3 + \cdots + y_n),$$

or

$$A < \frac{b}{n}(x_1 + x_2 + x_3 + \cdots + x_n),$$

or

$$A < \frac{b}{n}\left(\frac{b}{n} + \frac{2b}{n} + \frac{3b}{n} + \cdots + \frac{nb}{n}\right)$$

or, using the commutative law and the left-hand distributive law, we find

$$A < \frac{b^2}{n^2}(1 + 2 + 3 + \cdots + n).$$

But the sum again is an arithmetic progression and this gives us

$$A < \left(\frac{b^2}{n^2}\right)\left(\frac{n}{2}\right)(1 + n) = \left(\frac{b^2}{2}\right)\left(1 + \frac{1}{n}\right).$$

$$\therefore \quad A < \frac{b^2}{2} + \frac{b^2}{2n}.$$

Therefore, we have obtained a set of **upper bounds** for the area, taking $n = 1, 2, 3, \ldots$. This is a set of decreasing values as n increases, approaching a minimum of $b^2/2$. Therefore, we have proved that the answer is no more than $b^2/2$. We call $b^2/2$ the **least upper bound** of this set of upper bounds. Now we can write

$$A \leq \frac{b^2}{2}$$

$$\therefore \quad \frac{b^2}{2} \leq A \leq \frac{b^2}{2}$$

$$\therefore \quad A = \frac{b^2}{2}.$$

We observe that the greatest lower bound of one set and the least upper bound of another set are equal in this problem.

The answer only confirms a result which we already knew. But it establishes a procedure, which we shall now develop more fully.

At this point we make the following definition which may be used from here on, if desired.

Definition. $\displaystyle\sum_{i=1}^{n} a_i = a_1 + a_2 + a_3 + \cdots + a_n.$ That is, the sum of all the a's from a_1 to a_n inclusive.

For example,

$$\sum_{i=1}^{10} i = 1 + 2 + 3 + 4 + 5 + 6 + 7 + 8 + 9 + 10$$

$$\sum_{i=0}^{3} (i^2 + 1) = (0 + 1) + (1 + 1) + (4 + 1) + (9 + 1)$$

$$\sum_{i=1}^{5} y_i = y_1 + y_2 + y_3 + y_4 + y_5.$$

We now consider the area under the parabola $y = x^2$ and above the x axis, from $x = 0$ to $x = b$. We shall not take the special cases we used in the previous problem, but shall proceed to the general case, using Figure 12.

Again we divide the interval $0 \leq x \leq b$ into n equal parts so that the width of each subinterval is given by

$$h = \frac{b - 0}{n} = \frac{b}{n}$$

$$\therefore \quad x_0 = 0, \; x_1 = \frac{b}{n}, \; x_2 = \frac{2b}{n}, \; x_3 = \frac{3b}{n}, \ldots,$$

$$x_{n-1} = \frac{(n-1)b}{n}, \; x_n = \frac{nb}{n} = b.$$

Since the equation of the curve is $y = x^2$ we have

$$y_i = x_i^2, \quad i = 0, 1, 2, \ldots, n.$$

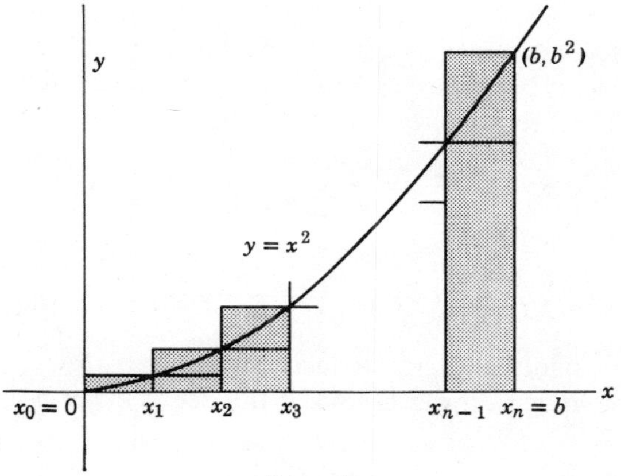

Figure 12

If we designate the area under the curve by A and take the sum of the areas of the inscribed rectangles we have the inequality

$$A > h(y_0 + y_1 + y_2 + y_3 + \cdots + y_{n-1}) = \sum_{i=0}^{n-1} hy_i$$

or

$$A > \frac{b}{n}(x_0^2 + x_1^2 + x_2^2 + x_3^2 + \cdots + x_{n-1}^2) = \frac{b}{n}\sum_{i=0}^{n-1} x_i^2$$

or

$$A > \frac{b}{n}\left\{0 + \left(\frac{b}{n}\right)^2 + \left(\frac{2b}{n}\right)^2 + \left(\frac{3b}{n}\right)^2 + \cdots + \left[\frac{(n-1)b}{n}\right]^2\right\}$$

or

$$A > \frac{b^3}{n^3}[1^2 + 2^2 + 3^2 + \cdots + (n-1)^2].$$

Now the sum in the parentheses is not an arithmetic progression, or a geometric progression for that matter. Let us suppose for the moment that we know the formula for the sum of the squares of the first k successive positive integers, namely

(1)
$$\frac{k(k+1)(2k+1)}{6} = 1^2 + 2^2 + 3^2 + \cdots + k^2.$$

Let us finish this problem and then return to a consideration of the verification of this and other similar formulas. Using formula (1) we obtain

$$A > \frac{b^3}{n^3}\left(\frac{(n-1)n(2n-1)}{6}\right)$$

$$= \frac{b^3}{6}\left(\frac{2n^3 - 3n^2 + n}{n^3}\right)$$

$$\therefore\ A > \frac{b^3}{3}\left(1 - \frac{3}{2n} + \frac{1}{2n^2}\right).$$

Since the second term is negative and the third is positive, it is not immediately clear that the right-hand side is increasing towards $b^3/3$ as n increases. Therefore, we write

$$\frac{-3}{2n} + \frac{1}{2n^2} = \frac{-3n + 1}{2n^2} < 0 \text{ for } n \geq 1.$$

Now we have

$$A > \frac{b^3}{3} - \frac{(b^3/3)(3n-1)}{2n^2}.$$

Therefore, the right-hand side is increasing toward $b^3/3$, as n increases, and $b^3/3$ is the greatest lower bound of this set of lower bounds.

$$\therefore\ A \geq \frac{b^3}{3}.$$

If we use the sum of the circumscribed rectangles we obtain

$$A < h(y_1 + y_2 + y_3 + \cdots + y_n) = h \sum_{i=1}^{n} y_i$$

or $\quad A < \dfrac{b}{n}(x_1{}^2 + x_2{}^2 + x_3{}^2 + \cdots + x_n{}^2) = \dfrac{b}{n} \sum_{i=1}^{n} x_i{}^2$

or $\quad A < \dfrac{b}{n}\left[\left(\dfrac{b}{n}\right)^2 + \left(\dfrac{2b}{n}\right)^2 + \left(\dfrac{3b}{n}\right)^2 + \cdots + \left(\dfrac{nb}{n}\right)^2\right]$

or $\quad A < \dfrac{b^3}{n^3}(1^2 + 2^2 + 3^2 + \cdots + n^2) = \left(\dfrac{b^3}{n^3}\right) \sum_{i=1}^{n} i^2.$

By using formula (1) this becomes

$$A < \frac{b^3}{n^3} \frac{n(n+1)(2n+1)}{6} = \frac{b^3}{6} \frac{2n^3 + 3n^2 + n}{n^3}$$

or $\quad A < \dfrac{b^3}{3}\left(1 + \dfrac{3}{2n} + \dfrac{1}{2n^2}\right).$

The right-hand side decreases toward $b^3/3$ as n increases and $b^3/3$ is the least upper bound of this set of upper bounds.

$$\therefore \quad A \leq \frac{b^3}{3}.$$

But since we have

$$\frac{b^3}{3} \leq A \leq \frac{b^3}{3}$$

it follows that

$$A = \frac{b^3}{3}.$$

Here is an exact formula for the area under the parabola, and we note its similarity to the area under the line $y = x$, namely $b^2/2$. (The expression "area under the curve" shall always imply "and above the x axis.")

Exercises

1. Find the exact area under the curve $y = x^3$ for $x = 0$ to $x = b$, using the fact that

$$\sum_{i=1}^{n} i^3 = 1^3 + 2^3 + 3^3 + \cdots + n^3 = \left[\frac{n(n+1)}{2}\right]^2.$$

2. Find the exact area under the curve $y = x^4$ for $x = 0$ to $x = b$, using the fact that

$$1^4 + 2^4 + 3^4 + \cdots + n^4 = \sum_{i=1}^{n} i^4 = \frac{n(n+1)(2n+1)(3n^2 + 3n - 1)}{30}.$$

3. In the problem for finding the area under $y = x^2$ from $x = 0$ to $x = b$, what is the least value of n for the inscribed area to be within $\frac{1}{64}$ of the correct answer? How close is the circumscribed area for the same n?

4. In problem 3 find the value of n such that the inscribed area differs from the value for $n - 1$ by less than $b^3/256$. By how much does the inscribed area for this n differ from the correct answer? What does this indicate?

5. In problem 2 determine whether the circumscribed area is always closer to the exact answer than the inscribed area or not.

6. Show that the difference between $b^2/2$ and $b^2/2 + b^2/2n$ can be made arbitrarily small for n large enough. Do the same for $b^3/3$ and

$$(b^3/3)[1 - (3n - 1)/2n^2].$$

2. Mathematical Induction

Now we return to formula (1). It is easy to establish its validity for any given positive integer k by direct substitution. For example,

$$k = 1, \quad \frac{1 \times 2 \times 3}{6} = 1^2$$

$$k = 2, \quad \frac{2 \times 3 \times 5}{6} = 1^2 + 2^2$$

$$k = 3, \quad \frac{3 \times 4 \times 7}{6} = 1^2 + 2^2 + 3^2.$$

But this is no proof, for there is no guarantee that the formula will hold for the next value k, no matter how high we go in selecting our values of k. For example, if we were to write in place of (1), the following formula

$$\frac{k(k + 1)(2k + 1)}{6} + (k - 1)(k - 2)(k - 3)(k - 4) \cdots (k - 100)$$

$$= 1^2 + 2^2 + 3^2 + \cdots + k^2$$

we see that this formula would give the same values as (1) for all k up to and including 100, since the new term would have a value of zero. But for $k = 101$ the formula would fail. It is evident that we could add a term to any formula that could be zero for any number of values of k, but not for all.

What we are looking for is the set of values of k for which the formula is true. What we would like to do is to be able to show that if it holds for any positive integer k that it must hold for $k + 1$, the next integer.

We consider some basic properties of positive integers. **The following is one of the postulates of positive integers. It is called the well-ordering principle.**

If a set S of positive integers contains one or more members then it

contains a smallest member. That is, there exists a positive integer, s, such that

$$s \leq n$$

for all n belonging to the set S.

For example, if we have a set

$$S: \ (26, 82, 35, 27, 19, 101)$$

then it contains a smallest member, namely 19.

If our set S is the set of all positive integers divisible by 3, then 3 is the smallest member.

With this postulate, as well as the definitions of inequality given previously, we can prove the following theorem.

Theorem 1. A set S of positive integers contains all of the positive integers if and only if the set S contains the integer 1 and contains the integer $(k + 1)$ whenever it contains the integer k.

PROOF. We prove the theorem by contradiction. Assume that S does not contain all of the positive integers. Let S' be the set of positive integers not contained in S, assuming that S' has at least one member. S' contains a smallest positive integer, by the well-ordering principle. Call this smallest integer s'. This $s' \neq 1$, since 1 is a member of S by hypothesis. But is $s' > 1$?

It looks logical, for we know of no positive integer less than one by experience, but this is no proof. And sometimes the more obvious the theorem, the less obvious the proof is. We prove the following:

Lemma. There are no positive integers between 0 and 1.

PROOF. Suppose there are positive integers between 0 and 1. Let t be the smallest one. Then

$$0 < t < 1.$$

But, multiplying by t, we obtain

$$0 < t^2 < t$$

from our properties of inequalities. Furthermore, t^2 is a positive integer, since the set of positive integers is closed under multiplication. But this contradicts the assumption that t is the smallest positive integer, for t^2 would be smaller. Therefore, there are no positive integers between 0 and 1. We now continue with the proof of our theorem.

We have $\qquad\qquad\qquad s' > 1.$

Therefore, $\qquad\qquad s' - 1 > 0.$

But $s' - 1$ does not belong to S', since s' is the smallest member of S'. Therefore, $s' - 1$ belongs to S, since it is the only other possibility. But, by hypothesis, if $s' - 1$ belongs to S then $(s' - 1) + 1$ belongs to S, since if k belongs to S then $(k + 1)$ belongs to S. But,

$$(s' - 1) + 1 = s' + (-1 + 1) = s' + 0 = s',$$

which belongs to S'. But since a positive integer cannot belong both to S and S', we have a contradiction. Therefore, S' contains no positive integers. Therefore S contains all of the positive integers, since S and S' together contained all positive integers by assumption.

To prove the "only if" condition we simply observe that if 1 does not belong to the set S, then the set does not contain all of the positive integers. And if $(k + 1)$ does not belong to the set S, whenever k does, then not all of the positive integers belong to the set S.

Now we have established the principle of **finite induction.** A formula, or statement, involving positive integers is to be proved true for all positive integers. We want to show that the set of positive integers, for which it is true, contains all of the positive integers. We check the formula, or statement, for its truth using the integer 1. If it is true, then 1 belongs to the set S of positive integers for which the formula is true. Now we assume that the formula is true for some integer k. Since it is true for $k = 1$, there exists at least one such integer. Now k belongs to the set of positive integers for which the formula is true. If we can now prove that the formula is true for the positive integer $(k + 1)$, then $(k + 1)$ belongs to the set S of positive integers for which the formula is true. By our theorem this set S contains all of the positive integers. And, therefore, our formula is true for all positive integers.

We illustrate with an example, asking for the set S of positive integers for which the following is true.

(2) $$(n/2)(n + 1) = 1 + 2 + 3 + \cdots + n.$$

We check this for $n = 1$, obtaining

$$(\tfrac{1}{2})(2) = 1$$

Therefore, the integer 1 belongs to the set S of positive integers for which the formula is true. Now we assume that (2) is true for some positive integer k. We repeat that this is a valid assumption, since we have just checked it for $k = 1$ and it holds. So there is at least one value of k for which the assumption is true. Naturally, the assumption may be made whether we know of any such value of k or not.

To show that it follows that (2) then holds when the positive integer $n = (k + 1)$, we add $(k + 1)$ to both sides of (2) with $n = k$, obtaining

(3) $$(k/2)(k + 1) + (k + 1) = 1 + 2 + 3 + \cdots + k + (k + 1).$$

Now the right-hand side is in the correct form of (2) when n is replaced by $(k + 1)$. The left-hand side should be of the form

$$\frac{(k + 1)(k + 2)}{2}.$$

To show that it actually is, we factor the left-hand side of (3), obtaining

$$(k + 1)\left(\frac{k}{2} + 1\right) = \frac{(k + 1)(k + 2)}{2}$$

which is the desired form. We have established the fact that (2) holds for the integer $(k + 1)$ whenever it holds for the integer k.

Therefore, the integer $(k + 1)$ belongs to the set of integers satisfying (2) whenever k does. By Theorem 1, the set of integers satisfying (2) contains all of the positive integers.

In the same way we prove

(4) $$\frac{n(n + 1)(2n + 1)}{6} = 1^2 + 2^2 + 3^2 + \cdots + n^2.$$

By substitution of $n = 1$, we obtain

$$\frac{1 \times 2 \times 3}{6} = 1^2.$$

Therefore, 1 belongs to the set S of integers for which the formula (4) is true. Now assume (4) is true for $n = k$. We add $(k + 1)^2$ to both sides, obtaining

$$\frac{k(k + 1)(2k + 1)}{6} + (k + 1)^2 = 1^2 + 2^2 + 3^2 + \cdots + k^2 + (k + 1)^2.$$

The right-hand side is what it should be if n is replaced by $(k + 1)$ in (4). Now we want the left-hand side to be of the form

$$\frac{(k + 1)(k + 2)(2k + 3)}{6}.$$

To show that it is, we factor the left-hand side, obtaining

$$(k + 1)\left[\frac{k(2k + 1)}{6} + (k + 1)\right]$$
$$= (k + 1)\frac{(2k^2 + 7k + 6)}{6} = \frac{(k + 1)(k + 2)(2k + 3)}{6}.$$

This verifies the formula when n is replaced by $(k + 1)$.

Now since $(k + 1)$ belongs to the set S of positive integers for which equation (4) is true whenever k belongs to S, then by Theorem 1 the set S contains all of the positive integers, and the formula is true for all positive integers.

Another type of example would be to prove that $a^n - b^n$ has a factor $a - b$ for all positive values of n.

We ask for the set S of positive integers for which this statement is true. Since it is true by inspection for $n = 1$, the set S contains 1. We assume that it is true for some integer $n = k$, i.e., we assume that

$$a^k - b^k = (a - b)P(a, b)$$

where $P(a, b)$ is some polynomial in a and b. Therefore k belongs to S. Now we write

$$
\begin{aligned}
a^{k+1} - b^{k+1} &= aa^k - bb^k \\
&= aa^k - ab^k + ab^k - bb^k \\
&= a(a^k - b^k) + b^k(a - b).
\end{aligned}
$$

By assumption, the first term has a factor of $a - b$; by inspection so does the second term.

$$\therefore \quad a^{k+1} - b^{k+1} \text{ has a factor of } a - b.$$

$$\therefore \quad k + 1 \text{ belongs to } S.$$

All positive integers belong to S, by the principle of mathematical induction. Therefore, the theorem is true for all positive integers.

The principle of finite induction is of great value in the proof of theorems in all parts of mathematics. It is important to note that both conditions of the theorem must be met (1 in S, and k in S implies $(k + 1)$ in S) before we can apply the theorem.

Exercises

Prove that the following equalities hold for all positive integers n.

1. $(\cos x + i \sin x)^n = \cos nx + i \sin nx$.

2. $1^4 + 2^4 + 3^4 + 4^4 + \cdots + n^4 = \dfrac{n(n + 1)(2n + 1)(3n^2 + 3n - 1)}{30}$.

3. $1 + r + r^2 + r^3 + \cdots + r^{n-1} = \dfrac{r^n - 1}{r - 1} = \displaystyle\sum_{i=0}^{n-1} r^i, \qquad r \neq 1$.

4. Show that $a + b$ is a factor of $a^{2n+1} + b^{2n+1}$.

5. Show that $n(n + 1)(n + 2)$ is divisible by 6.

6. What is the relation between the sum of the first n integers and the sum of their cubes?

7. Show that $2^n \geq 2n$.

3. A Generalized Area Problem

In the problems in the text and in the exercises it should be evident that a nice pattern is developing for the areas under the curves $y = x^k$ from $x = 0$ to $x = b$.

$$k = 1, \qquad A = b^2/2$$
$$k = 2, \qquad A = b^3/3$$
$$k = 3, \qquad A = b^4/4.$$

The difficulty in extending these results in the same way is dependent upon the formula for the sum of the kth powers of the positive integers. We now indicate a way around the difficulty.

It will be noticed that in the areas computed so far that the interval along the x axis has been divided into equal parts. It will be shown that this is neither necessary nor desirable in some problems.

In order to find the area under the curve $y = x^k$ from $x = a$ to $x = b$, we shall divide our interval into unequal parts. But, in order that there may be a workable pattern, we shall use a geometric progression. See Figure 13.

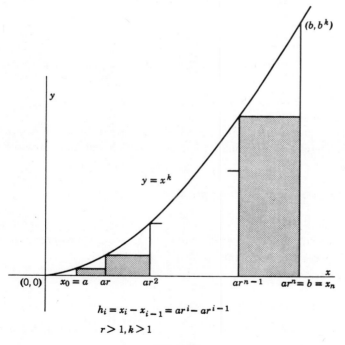

$$h_i = x_i - x_{i-1} = ar^i - ar^{i-1}$$
$$r > 1, k > 1$$

Figure 13

Using the inscribed rectangles, we find

$$A > h_1 y_0 + h_2 y_1 + h_3 y_2 + \cdots + h_n y_{n-1}$$
$$A > (ar - a)a^k + (ar^2 - ar)(ar)^k + \cdots + (ar^n - ar^{n-1})(ar^{n-1})^k$$
$$A > a^{k+1}(r - 1)[1 + r^{k+1} + r^{2(k+1)} + \cdots + r^{(n-1)(k+1)}].$$

Since the sum in the brackets is a geometric progression, with a ratio of r^{k+1}, we may write it as a single term giving us

$$A > a^{k+1}(r - 1) \frac{r^{n(k+1)} - 1}{r^{k+1} - 1}.$$

Since the answer must depend upon b and the subdivision is prescribed such that

$$x_n = ar^n = b,$$

we can substitute for r^n, recalling that

$$r^{n(k+1)} = (r^n)^{k+1},$$

obtaining

$$A > a^{k+1}(r - 1) \frac{[(b/a)^{k+1} - 1]}{r^{k+1} - 1} = \frac{(r - 1)(b^{k+1} - a^{k+1})}{r^{k+1} - 1}.$$

But $r^{k+1} - 1$ is divisible by $r - 1$, giving us

$$A > \frac{b^{k+1} - a^{k+1}}{r^k + r^{k-1} + r^{k-2} + \cdots + 1}$$

or a set of lower bounds for the area, each one corresponding to a value of r, which depends upon n.

But, as n approaches infinity, the width of each subinterval approaches zero, and therefore r approaches 1, since any subinterval is of width

$$ar^i - ar^{i-1} = ar^{i-1}(r - 1).$$

However, we note that the expression

$$r^k + r^{k-1} + r^{k-2} + \cdots + 1$$

has $k + 1$ terms and, since each term approaches 1 as r approaches 1, the sum decreases to a lower limit of $k + 1$, since $r > 1$.

Therefore, we have

$$A \geq \frac{b^{k+1} - a^{k+1}}{k + 1},$$

and this is the greatest lower bound of the set of lower bounds for the area under the curve.

Using circumscribed rectangles we would obtain

$$A \le \frac{b^{k+1} - a^{k+1}}{k + 1},$$

the least upper bound, which is left as an exercise for the student.

From the previous result we have

$$\frac{b^{k+1} - a^{k+1}}{k + 1} \le A \le \frac{b^{k+1} - a^{k+1}}{k + 1}.$$

$$\therefore \quad A = \frac{b^{k+1} - a^{k+1}}{k + 1}.$$

For $a = 0$ one obtains

$$A = \frac{b^{k+1}}{k + 1}$$

which gives us the general result that we had anticipated somewhat from the earlier special cases.

Now it should be observed that there might be many curves for which the same approach could be used. However, there is no guarantee that the limits could be achieved as readily, if at all, as in the problems already considered. But there would be nothing to prevent a numerical approximation to the given area being made by computing the sum of the areas of the inscribed and circumscribed rectangles for a given n. This would give both an upper and lower bound to the actual result. If the difference between the two results is greater than the maximum error allowed, then a larger value of n could be selected and the process continued until the desired accuracy was achieved.

Naturally the time required to do the calculations might soon become excessive. In such a case we turn to the electronic computer to speed up the work, and to make calculations not feasible by hand. We shall explore this possibility later in the chapter.

Exercises

1. Find the least upper bound of the set of upper bounds for the area under the curve $y = x^k$ from $x = a$ to $x = b$ by the method of this section.

2. Why was it necessary to take an interval $a \le x \le b$ instead of $0 \le x \le b$, in the previous problem?

3. Find values of r and n such that the area of the inscribed rectangles differs from the true area by less than $(b^2 - a^2)/32$ for $k = 1$.

4. Can any statement be made regarding whether the area of the inscribed rectangles is closer to the exact area than the area of the circumscribed rectangles?

5. What restrictions are placed on k in the proof of example 1?

6. From the general results, derived in this section, find the area under the curve

$$y = 2x^3 + 3x^2 - 1 \qquad 1 \le x \le 3$$

and above the x axis.

7. From the general results find the area under the curve

$$y = x^{\frac{1}{2}} \qquad 0 \le x \le 1.$$

8. (a) From the general results, find the area between the curve

$$y = 2 + x - x^2 \qquad -1 \le x \le 2.$$

and the x axis.

(b) Can you do the same problem for $-1 \le x \le 3$? What difficulties are encountered?

4. Area under the Sine Curve

Now let us turn to a consideration of areas bounded by trigonometric curves. We shall use the same fundamental process which we have used up to this point.

Consider the curve

$$y = \sin x;$$

we shall determine the exact area bounded by this curve, the x axis and the line $x = b$, where $b = \pi/2$.

$$h = \frac{b - 0}{n} = \frac{b}{n} = x_i - x_{i-1}$$

$$y_i = \sin x_i, \ i = 0, 1, 2, \ldots, n.$$

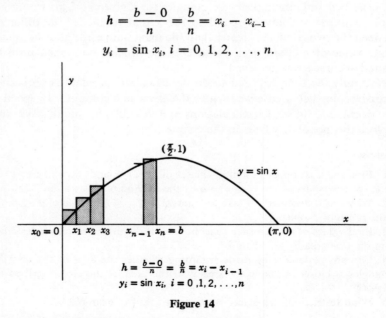

$$h = \frac{b-0}{n} = \frac{b}{n} = x_i - x_{i-1}$$
$$y_i = \sin x_i, \ i = 0, 1, 2, \ldots, n$$

Figure 14

122   EQUALITIES AND APPROXIMATIONS

We take the sum of the areas of the circumscribed rectangles and obtain

$$A < h(y_1 + y_2 + y_3 + \cdots + y_n)$$

$$A < \frac{b}{n}\left(\sin\frac{b}{n} + \sin\frac{2b}{n} + \sin\frac{3b}{n} + \cdots + \sin\frac{nb}{n}\right)$$

or

$$A < \frac{b}{n}\sum_{i=1}^{n}\sin\frac{ib}{n}.$$

The sum in parentheses is neither an arithmetic nor a geometric progression, so we must use some other procedure to find the sum. We note that b/n approaches zero as n approaches infinity, and that this is either the angle or a divisor of the angle in all of the terms in the parentheses; we recall that we know that

$$\lim_{\theta \to 0}\frac{\theta}{\sin\theta} = 1.$$

Perhaps then we might multiply and divide our expression by $\sin b/n$ so that our limit will not be zero. It turns out that this reasoning is sound, but that it is better to multiply and divide by $\sin b/2n$ instead of b/n. The student should check the other possibility. Now we have

$$A < \frac{b}{n}\left(\sin\frac{b}{n} + \sin\frac{2b}{n} + \sin\frac{3b}{n} + \cdots + \sin\frac{nb}{n}\right)\frac{\sin b/2n}{\sin b/2n}.$$

In order to simplify the expression above, we turn to the formulas of trigonometry and, in particular, consider the following

$$\sin x \sin y = \tfrac{1}{2}[\cos(x - y) - \cos(x + y)].$$

Applying this to the expression above, we obtain

$$A < \frac{\dfrac{b}{2n}\left\{\left(\cos\dfrac{b}{2n} - \cos\dfrac{3b}{2n}\right) + \left(\cos\dfrac{3b}{2n} - \cos\dfrac{5b}{2n}\right) + \cdots + \left[\cos\dfrac{(2n-1)b}{2n} - \cos\dfrac{(2n+1)b}{2n}\right]\right\}}{\sin\dfrac{b}{2n}}.$$

Note that the sum of the second and third terms is zero, as well as the fourth and fifth, and so on up to and including the next to the last term. We obtain

$$A < \frac{b/2n}{\sin b/2n}\left[\cos\frac{b}{2n} - \cos\frac{(2n+1)b}{2n}\right]$$

or

$$A < \frac{b/2n}{\sin b/2n} \left[\cos \frac{b}{2n} - \cos \left(1 + \frac{1}{2n} \right) b \right].$$

For each value of n, we have an upper bound for A. We are interested in determining the least upper bound.

Now taking the limit as n approaches infinity, we have

$$\lim_{n \to \infty} \frac{b/2n}{\sin b/2n} = 1.$$

This could be clarified, perhaps, by substituting $t = b/2n$. Then we have

$$\lim_{n \to \infty} \frac{b}{2n} = \lim_{t \to 0} t = 0.$$

$$\therefore \quad \lim_{n \to \infty} \frac{b/2n}{\sin b/2n} = \lim_{t \to 0} \frac{t}{\sin t} = 1.$$

Then in the same way,

$$\lim_{n \to \infty} \cos \frac{b}{2n} = \cos 0 = 1$$

$$\lim_{n \to \infty} \cos \left(1 + \frac{1}{2n} \right) b = \cos b.$$

Since $b/2n$ decreases as n increases, then $\cos b/2n$ increases. Since $1 + 1/2n$ decreases as n increases, then $\cos (1 + 1/2n)b$ increases.

Since both $\cos b/2n$ and $\cos (1 + 1/2n)b$ increase as n increases, it is not possible to determine by inspection whether their difference increases or decreases. Therefore, we use the following formula from trigonometry.

$$\cos x - \cos y = 2 \left(\sin \frac{y + x}{2} \right) \sin \frac{y - x}{2}$$

$$\therefore \quad \cos \frac{b}{2n} - \cos \left(1 + \frac{1}{2n} \right) b = 2 \left[\sin b \left(\frac{1 + 1/n}{2} \right) \sin \frac{b}{2} \right].$$

Since $b(1 + 1/n)/2$ decreases as n increases, $\sin b(1 + 1/n)/2$ decreases also.

We know from Section 5 of Chapter 5 that $\theta/\sin \theta > 1$ and decreases toward 1 as θ decreases towards zero. Therefore,

$$\frac{b/2n}{\sin b/2n} > 1$$

and decreases toward 1 as n increases.

Using these results, we see that the set of upper bounds for A decrease, as n increases, to a least upper bound $1 - \cos b$, and we have

$$A \leq 1 - \cos b.$$

The problem of the inscribed rectangles is left to the student as an exercise.

But, assuming that the greatest lower bound is equal to the least upper bound, we would have

$$A = 1 - \cos b$$

as the area under the sine curve and above the x axis for the interval $0 \leq x \leq b$.

It might have been expected that the result would be expressible in terms of a trigonometric function and especially the cosine, as the cosine is so closely related to the sine.

It is of interest to note that not only when $b = 0$, $A = 0$, consistent with the expected result, but that for $b = \pi/2$, $A = 1$. Since the sine curve is symmetrical with respect to the line $x = \pi/2$, the formula above is valid for the entire interval $0 \leq x \leq \pi$. And the entire area under one arch of the sine curve and above the x axis is exactly two square units.

The area under the curve $y = \cos x$ can be found in the same way. This is left as an exercise for the student.

Exercises

1. In the problem in the text on p. 123 try multiplying and dividing by $\sin b/n$ instead of $\sin b/2n$.

2. Find the greatest lower bound for the area in the same way as the least upper bound was determined. Can you show that as n increases, the lower bounds (which depend upon n) increase to an upper limit (independent of n)? What is the difficulty?

3. Why was the value of b restricted to values less than $\pi/2$ in the proof?

4. Using your trig tables, determine how close the area of the inscribed rectangles is to the exact area for $n = 4$ and $b = \pi/2$.

5. Solve the complete problem for the area under the curve

$$y = \cos x \qquad 0 \leq x \leq b$$
$$b \leq \pi/2$$

and above the x axis.

6. What is the relation between the answers found in the case of the cosine and sine curves?

7. What can be said about the area under any arch of the sine or cosine curve?

8. Write all sums in this chapter using the $\sum$ notation.

5. Fortran Programs

It is evident from the preceding discussion that the method of approximating areas by rectangles may lead to the exact result, but that the algebra involved will be the determining factor. However, the method will always make it possible to find an upper and a lower bound for the area. The practical question is whether or not the difference between the upper and lower bounds can be made small enough to obtain the desired degree of accuracy.

For example, in Section 1 of this chapter we determined, for a given value of n, a lower bound for the area under the curve $y = x^2$ as

$$\text{l.b.} = \left(\frac{b^3}{n^3}\right)[1^2 + 2^2 + 3^2 + \cdots + (n-1)^2]$$

and an upper bound as

$$\text{u.b.} = \left(\frac{b^3}{n^3}\right)(1^2 + 2^2 + 3^2 + \cdots + n^2).$$

If $b = 3$ and $n = 100$, we obtain

$$\text{l.b.} = 8.86545 \qquad \text{and} \qquad \text{u.b.} = 9.13545.$$

The difference between these values is 0.27 and it appears that our accuracy cannot even be guaranteed to the nearest tenth. If we did not have a formula to calculate the sum of the squares of the first 100 integers, this would have been an ardous task. Even with a desk calculator the problem is lengthy.

When one desires very great accuracy in such problems, the use of an electronic computer is almost a must. We will illustrate, using the preceding problem, the kind of Fortran program which might be used.

The only part of the program which is not completely straightforward is the calculation of the sum of the squares of the integers. However, this is not difficult if one recalls that only two numbers may be added together at a time. Thus we add 1^2 to 2^2 and then add the sum to 3^2 and that sum to 4^2 and so on. But, in order to begin our addition, we need to know the value of the first number to be added.

We shall do the problem completely in floating-point, so as not to restrict the size of our numbers. We use CN for n, B for b, AC for upper bound, AI for lower bound, TOL for the accuracy desired, SUM1 for sum of squares of first $n - 1$ integers and SUM2 for sum of squares of first n integers. Our flow chart follows.

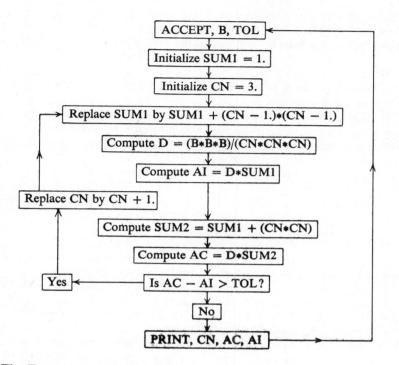

The Fortran program would be as follows

```
1 ACCEPT, B, TOL
  SUM1 = 1.
  CN = 3.
4 SUM1 = SUM1 + (CN - 1.)*(CN - 1.)
  D = (B*B*B)/(CN*CN*CN)
  AI = D*SUM1
  SUM2 = SUM1 + (CN*CN)
  AC = D*SUM2
  IF ((AC - AI) - TOL) 2, 2, 3
3 CN = CN + 1.
  GO TO 4
2 PRINT, CN, AI, AC
  GO TO 1
  END
```

If it were felt that fixed-point numbers would speed up the computation in finding SUM1, we would have the problem of a mixed-mode expression, and fixed point could not be used in finding D, AI, or AC. In some problems the effect of changing CN by 1. might be so negligible that thought should be given to doubling CN each time, or changing it by any multiple. Such a possibility is left to the exercises.

Exercises

1. Write a program to determine the area under $y = x^3$, from $x = 0$ to $x = b$, to any desired degree of accuracy.

2. Write a program to determine the area under $y = x^k$, from $x = a$ to $x = b$, using equal subdivisions, and also geometric progressions as given in Section 3 of this chapter. Do not assume in either case that the sums can be expressed by formula. Assume k is a positive integer.

3. Modify the program written in Section 5 in order to allow CN to be doubled each time.

4. Write a program to verify for $n = 1, 2, 3, \ldots, N$ that the expression

$$\frac{(b/2n)}{\sin b/2n}\left[\cos\frac{b}{2n} - \cos\left(1 - \frac{1}{2n}\right)b\right]$$

seems to be increasing as n increases, even though the first factor is decreasing and always greater than 1. See Exercise 2 in Section 4 of this chapter.

5. Write a program for determining the area under the cosine curve, from $x = 0$ to $x = b$, not assuming that the sum of terms can be expressed by a formula. Use the subroutines for finding $\sin x$ and $\cos x$. See Chapter 3.

6. Write a program for finding the area under the sine curve, from $x = 0$ to $x = b$, using geometric progressions for subdivisions and compare answers for equal subdivisions for the same value of n. Use appropriate subroutines.

7. Write a program for finding the area under $y = \log_e x$, from $x = 1$ to $x = b$, using equal subdivisions. Use the subroutines for $\log_e x$.

8. Write a program for determining the area under $y = \tan x$, from $x = 0$ to $x = b$, using the appropriate subroutine. What is the restriction on b?

7 NUMERICAL AND POLYNOMIAL APPROXIMATIONS

1. Iterative Methods

In the preceding chapter we have considered sets of lower (or upper) bounds of areas which approached a greatest lower (or least upper) bound as a limit as the integer n approached infinity. We could have written

$$A_n = \frac{b/2n}{\sin b/2n}\left[\cos \frac{b}{2n} - \cos \frac{(2n + 1)b}{2n}\right],$$

where A_n stands for the nth upper bound of the area under the curve $y = \sin x$ from $x = 0$ to $x = b$.

We recall that the exact area A and the least upper bound were both found to be $1 - \cos b$ and, therefore, we would write

$$A = \lim_{n \to \infty} A_n.$$

In other words, the larger the value of n the closer A_n is to the exact area A.

It would be convenient to know the relation between the values of A_n for two different values of n. This would allow the calculation of the value of A_n for one value of n in terms of its value for some other n, and might simplify the calculation. It would also give a measure of the change in A_n as n changed.

In the preceding example this does not appear to be possible in a simple form. Let us illustrate with another example how we might find such a relation. Consider the problem for the area under the curve $y = x$ from $x = 0$ to $x = b$. We found for circumscribed rectangles

$$A_n = \frac{b^2}{2} + \frac{b^2}{2n}$$

$$\therefore \quad \frac{2A_n}{b^2} - 1 = \frac{1}{n}$$

or

$$\frac{b^2}{2A_n - b^2} = n$$

$$\therefore \quad \frac{b^2}{2A_{n+1} - b^2} = n + 1.$$

Substituting from the previous equation for n and solving for A_{n+1} we obtain

(1)
$$A_{n+1} = b^2\left(1 - \frac{b^2}{4A_n}\right).$$

This is called a **recurrence relation**. We know that $A_1 = b^2$ from Figure 8 in Section 1 of Chapter 6. From equation (1) we find, using $n = 1$,

$$A_2 = \frac{3b^2}{4},$$

then using (1) again we find, using $n = 2$,

$$A_3 = \frac{2b^2}{3};$$

and then, using $n = 3$,

$$A_4 = \frac{5b^2}{8}.$$

This checks with the value obtained in Section 1 of Chapter 6 for four circumscribed rectangles.

Such a method is called an **iteration**. It has wide applicability as is shown in the following case.

Suppose that we ask for the square root of a number A. We could guess at the square root, square our guess and check the result with A to determine the accuracy. However, if our first guess is not close enough, how can we use it to gain greater accuracy, rather than just making another arbitrary guess? Let us call G the guess and assume

$$G > \sqrt{A}.$$

Then
$$\frac{A}{G} < \sqrt{A}.$$

If we average these two values we have

(2)
$$S = \frac{A/G + G}{2}$$

where
$$\frac{A}{G} < S < G.$$

But is S any closer to $\sqrt{A}$ than G was? We illustrate first with an example.

Let $A = 16$ and take $G = 8$. Clearly $G > \sqrt{A}$. Using (2),

$$S = \frac{16/8 + 8}{2} = 5,$$

and
$$2 < 5 < 8.$$

We see that 5 is closer to $\sqrt{A}$ than G was. If we select $G = 5$, we obtain, using (2),

$$S = \frac{16/5 + 5}{2} = 4.1.$$

We see that 4.1 is closer to $\sqrt{A}$ than 5 was.

Let us attempt to prove that if $G > \sqrt{A}$, then S is closer to $\sqrt{A}$ than G was.

Select $G = b\sqrt{A}$, $b > 1$. Using (2)

$$S = \frac{A/b\sqrt{A} + b\sqrt{A}}{2}$$

$$\therefore \quad S = \frac{(1/b + b)\sqrt{A}}{2} = c\sqrt{A}$$

where
$$c = \frac{1/b + b}{2}.$$

Now $S < G$ if $c < b$. Therefore, we consider

$$b - c = b - \frac{1/b + b}{2}$$

$$= \frac{b^2 - 1}{2b} > 0,$$

since $b > 1$. Therefore, $c < b$ by definition of inequalities. But is $S > \sqrt{A}$ also? It will be if $c > 1$. We consider

$$c - 1 = \frac{1/b + b}{2} - 1$$

$$= \frac{(b - 1)^2}{2b} > 0.$$

NUMERICAL AND POLYNOMIAL APPROXIMATIONS   131

(Why?)

$$\therefore \quad c > 1.$$

$$\therefore \quad \sqrt{A} < S < G.$$

Since we have proved that if our guess G is greater than $\sqrt{A}$ and that then S will be greater than $\sqrt{A}$ also and closer to $\sqrt{A}$ than G was, we can now state that S is a good second guess; and clearly S depends upon G. Furthermore, the process can be repeated indefinitely.

There are two unanswered questions. First, if $G < \sqrt{A}$, what can be said about S? Second, if we continue the iteration, will S become arbitrarily close to $\sqrt{A}$? Both of these questions are left to the student to answer with a proof.

It is now suggested that (2) can be written as

$$(3) \qquad G_{n+1} = \frac{A/G_n + G_n}{2}, \qquad n = 1, 2, 3, \dots$$

and a process of iteration will lead to any desired degree of accuracy for the $\sqrt{A}$, no matter how poor a guess we make as G_1.

Exercises

1. In Section 1 of Chapter 6 try to find the simplest possible relation between A_n and A_{n+1} for the set of upper bounds for the area under the curve $y = x^2$, $0 \le x \le b$.

2. Instead of the recurrence relation (1) in this section, can you find the relation between A_{2n} and A_n for the same area problem?

3. Using recurrence relation (3) prove that G_{n+1} can be made arbitrarily close to $\sqrt{A}$ if n is taken large enough, no matter what G_1 is. Hint: Compare $G_{n+1} - \sqrt{A}$ with $G_n - \sqrt{A}$. What is the result when $G_1 = \sqrt{A}$?

4. Would $S = (A/G^2 + G)/2$ be a good recurrence relation for finding $\sqrt[3]{A}$? Prove your answer. (Expect the proof to be similar but much more involved than in the case of the square root.) What is the result when $G = \sqrt[3]{A}$?

5. Approximate the area of a unit circle with regular, inscribed polygons of n sides, using the fact that the area of a triangle is one-half the product of two sides and the sine of the included angle. If A_n is a lower bound, prove that

$$A_{2n} = \frac{A_n}{\cos \pi/n}, \qquad n \ge 3.$$

6. Using the result of exercise 5 and the fact that $A_4 = 2$, find a formula for π in terms of an infinite product of cosines. Use the half-angle formula to write this in terms of $\cos \pi/4$. Use the fact that $\lim_{n \to \infty} A_{2n} = \pi$.

2. Approximation of $\sqrt{x}$

In the preceding section we have found a way to calculate the square root of a number to within a prescribed tolerance, but the process must be repeated for each such number. Furthermore, the method is not useful if one is working with the equation

$$y = x^{1/2}$$

and wishes to keep x as a variable.

The question arises as to whether the expression $x^{1/2}$ can be written in some other form that may be suitable for numerical calculation or algebraic manipulation. One form that appears to satisfy such requirements is the polynomial

$$\sum_{i=0}^{n} a_i x^i = a_0 + a_1 x + a_2 x^2 + \cdots + a_n x^n = P_n(x).$$

There are two basic reasons for such a choice. First, the value of a given polynomial, for a given value of x, involves only the basic operations of addition and multiplication. Second, we have already experienced complete success in finding the area under any curve represented by a polynomial equation. This implies that polynomials may be appropriate approximations for a variety of mathematical forms.

Consider

$$y = x^{1/2}, \qquad 0 \leq x \leq 1.$$

Now we ask what degree polynomial should be selected and how the coefficients shall be determined for the interval $0 \leq x \leq 1$. If the value of the polynomial is to be exact when $x = 0$, then the constant term must be zero. So the polynomial must be at least of the first degree. If the polynomial is of the first degree and is to be exact for $x = 1$, we must have

$$y \approx P_1(x) = x, \qquad 0 \leq x \leq 1.$$

(The wavy equal signs denote approximately equal.)

However, this approximation is not exact when $x = \frac{1}{2}$, for example, as

$$P_1(\tfrac{1}{2}) = \tfrac{1}{2} = 0.5$$

and

$$y = 1/\sqrt{2} = 0.707,$$

for $x = \frac{1}{2}$.

We have an error of -0.207 to three decimal places. Since $x^{1/2} = x$ for $x = 0$ and $x = 1$ only, we see by the example above that

$$y \geq P_1(x), \qquad 0 \leq x \leq 1.$$

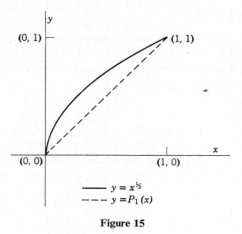

$$\begin{array}{l} \text{——} \quad y = x^{\frac{1}{2}} \\ \text{———} \quad y = P_1(x) \end{array}$$

Figure 15

The graphs of the two curves are shown below in Figure 15. (From here on all approximating curves will be drawn with dotted lines.)

We shall set our criterion for accuracy of approximation as follows. If

$$y = P_n(x) \qquad \text{for} \quad x = x_1$$

and $$y = P_n(x) \qquad \text{for} \quad x = x_2$$

and $$x_3 = (x_1 + x_2)/2$$

then $|y - P_n(x)|$ shall be less than T, for $x = x_3$, where T is the prescribed tolerance. (There are many different ways in which the accuracy may be prescribed. The present selection is only an illustration and is reasonable if the original curve has no high peaks or low dips, in the interval being considered, and does not rise or fall too steeply.)

Naturally, the smaller the value of $|x_1 - x_2|$ the better the approximation. Furthermore, one would want to check the accuracy at more than the midpoint in many cases, for the greatest error will not necessarily occur at the midpoint. There are countless refinements which may be made in order to give greater accuracy. The purpose here is to introduce the topic and its potential use.

In our present problem let us set $T = 0.1$ and continue until we reach this accuracy. For each midpoint at which the accuracy is not fulfilled, we shall increase the degree of the polynomial by 1 and ask that the new polynomial have the same value as $x^{\frac{1}{2}}$ at each of these midpoints.

It is evident that a polynomial $P_n(x)$ of the nth degree has $n + 1$ coefficients and, therefore, $n + 1$ conditions may be placed on it. Graphically, this means that the curve may be required to pass through $n + 1$ points.

In our particular problem we have placed two conditions on our first-degree polynomial, that it be exact at $x = 0$ and at $x = 1$. We now require that our approximating polynomial also be exact at $x = \frac{1}{2}$. This will require that the polynomial be of the second degree. We write

$$y \approx P_2(x) = a_0 + a_1 x + a_2 x^2, \ 0 \le x \le 1.$$

Our conditions are

$$P_2(0) = 0, \ P_2(\tfrac{1}{2}) = 1/\sqrt{2}, \ P_2(1) = 1.$$

$$\therefore \quad a_0 = 0$$

$$a_1/2 + a_2/4 = 1/\sqrt{2}$$

$$a_1 + a_2 = 1.$$

Solving these equations we obtain

$$a_1 = -1 + 2\sqrt{2} \text{ and } a_2 = 2(1 - \sqrt{2})$$

$$\therefore \quad y \approx P_2(x) = (-1 + 2\sqrt{2})x + 2(1 - \sqrt{2})x^2, \qquad 0 \le x \le 1.$$

To see whether our requirement for accuracy is satisfied, we check the values of the polynomial for $x = \frac{1}{4}$ and $x = \frac{3}{4}$:

$$P_2(\tfrac{1}{4}) = (3\sqrt{2} - 1)/8, \ y = \tfrac{1}{2}$$

$$|y - P_2(\tfrac{1}{4})| = |(5 - 3\sqrt{2})/8| = |0.095| < 0.1$$

$$P_2(\tfrac{3}{4}) = 3(1 + \sqrt{2})/8, \ y = \sqrt{3}/2$$

$$|y - P_2(\tfrac{3}{4})| = |(-3 + 4\sqrt{3} - 3\sqrt{2})/8| = |-0.039| < 0.1.$$

Our accuracy is satisfied, and we note also that

$$y \ge P_2(x), \qquad 0 \le x \le \tfrac{1}{2}$$

$$y \le P_2(x), \qquad \tfrac{1}{2} \le x \le 1.$$

The graphs are shown in Figure 16.

To show the necessity of our comment on when this might not be a reasonable approximation, consider the value of y and of the polynomial for $x = \frac{1}{16}$.

$$P_2(\tfrac{1}{16}) = (-7 + 15\sqrt{2})/128 = 0.111$$

$$y = \tfrac{1}{4}$$

$$\therefore \quad |y - P_2(\tfrac{1}{16})| = 0.139.$$

But this is greater than our tolerance which was satisfied at the midpoints. We note that the square root of a number less than 1 is greater than the number. As a matter of fact the square root of $\frac{1}{16}$ is four times the number,

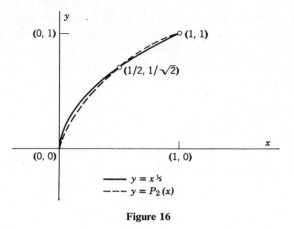

$$\begin{array}{l}\text{------ } y = x^{\frac{1}{2}} \\ \text{---- } y = P_2(x)\end{array}$$

Figure 16

and we see that the curve rises very steeply at this point, inasmuch as the ordinate is four times the abscissa.

However, consider the values at $x = 15/16$, where the curve is much flatter. We find

$$P_2\left(\frac{15}{16}\right) = \frac{105 + 15\sqrt{2}}{128} = 0.986$$

$$y = \frac{\sqrt{15}}{16} = 0.968$$

$$\therefore \quad \left| y - P_2\left(\frac{15}{16}\right) \right| = |-0.018| < 0.1,$$

which is well within our tolerance. We see that great changes in the rate of change of the ordinate with respect to the abscissa may influence our accuracy, but the higher the degree of $P_n(x)$ the less this is so.

Exercises

1. If the tolerance in the problem in this section is changed to 0.03, what must the degree of the approximating polynomial be? Leave the coefficients of the polynomial in terms of radicals.

2. Find the greatest possible increase required in the degree of the approximating polynomial when the accuracy is not met at some step.

3. Find a polynomial approximation to

$$y = x^{\frac{1}{3}}, \qquad 0 \leq x \leq 1$$

with $T = 0.2$. Leave the coefficients in terms of radicals.

4. Find a polynomial approximation to

$$y = x^{\frac{1}{2}}, \qquad 1 \leq x \leq 2$$

with $T = 0.1$; $T = 0.05$. Leave the coefficients in terms of radicals. Compare the degrees required with those for the same problem with the interval $0 \le x \le 1$. Can any general comment be made?

5. Find the polynomial approximation to $y = 1/(1 + x^2)$, exact for $x = 0$, $\frac{1}{2}$, 1. The area under this curve and above the x axis for $0 \le x \le 1$ is exactly $\pi/4$. Using the area formulas previously developed, determine how close the area under the polynomial is to $\pi/4$.

3. Approximation of sin x

The trigonometric expressions may be represented by polynomial approximations in the same way as in the preceding section. Actually we have had some experience with this particular problem. Recall once again that we proved

$$\lim_{x \to 0} \frac{\sin x}{x} = 1.$$

In effect, we have proved that

$$\sin x \approx x,$$

for x close to zero. Therefore, we have a first-degree polynomial approximation to sin x, but the question is as to the interval over which it can be used.

Naturally the given tolerance will be a controlling factor, but there is another. Suppose, for example, we tried

$$y = \sin x \approx P_1(x) = x, \qquad 0 \le x \le \pi/2.$$

This would give

$$P_1(\pi/2) = \pi/2 = 1.57 > 1,$$

but this is nonsense, as the sin x never exceeds 1 in value. Again the graph illustrates the point very well, as in Figure 17.

We see that the approximation steadily becomes worse as x increases. Our problem will be to find a polynomial approximation, accurate by our requirements, over the interval $0 \le x \le \pi/2$.

Our first thought might be to consider a first-degree polynomial, exact for $x = 0$ and $x = \pi/2$, and then go to a second-degree polynomial, if this is not accurate enough at the midpoint, etc. But sin x has other properties which should be considered.

For example,

$$\sin(-x) = -\sin x.$$

This property could not possibly hold for a second-degree polynomial as if

$$P_2(x) = a_0 + a_1 x + a_2 x^2, \qquad a_2 \ne 0$$

then

$$P_2(-x) = a_0 - a_1 x + a_2 x^2 \ne -P_2(x).$$

If this property does not interest us, then we would proceed as usual, but observe that if we can preserve this property then our approximation will not only hold in the positive interval, but in the corresponding negative interval as well. This would be of great advantage in some problems.

It is left as an exercise to prove that we must have a polynomial with only odd powers to satisfy this additional requirement.

We write

$$y \approx P_1(x) = a_1 x, \qquad 0 \le x \le \pi/2,$$

subject to the conditions

$$P_1(0) = 0, \; P_1(\pi/2) = 1$$

and $T = 0.01$. We find

$$P_1(x) = (2/\pi)x, \qquad 0 \le x \le \pi/2$$

but for $x = \pi/4$,

$$P_1(\pi/4) = \tfrac{1}{2}, \qquad y = 1/\sqrt{2}.$$
$$\therefore \quad |y - P_1(\pi/4)| = |1/\sqrt{2} - \tfrac{1}{2}| = |0.207| > 0.01.$$

Our conditions on accuracy are not satisfied, and we write

$$y \approx P_3(x) = a_1 x + a_3 x^3, \qquad 0 \le x \le \pi/2$$

subject to the conditions

$$P_3(0) = 0, \; P_3(\pi/4) = 1/\sqrt{2}, \; P_3(\pi/2) = 1.$$
$$\therefore \quad a_1 \pi/4 + a_3(\pi/4)^3 = 1/\sqrt{2}$$
$$a_1 \pi/2 + a_3(\pi/2)^3 = 1.$$

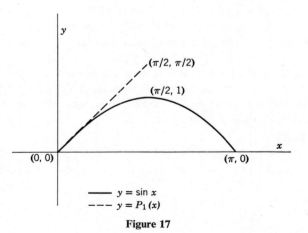

Figure 17

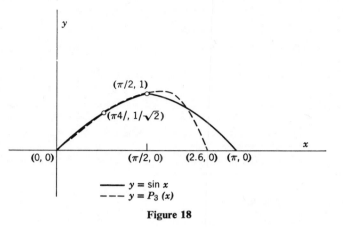

$y = \sin x$
$y = P_3(x)$

Figure 18

Solving these equations we obtain

$$a_1 = \frac{2(4\sqrt{2} - 1)}{3\pi}, \quad a_3 = \frac{32(1 - \sqrt{2})}{3\pi^3}$$

$$\therefore \quad y \approx P_3(x) = \left(\frac{2(4\sqrt{2} - 1)}{3\pi}\right)x + \left(\frac{32(1 - \sqrt{2})}{3\pi^3}\right)x^3, \quad 0 \le x \le \pi/2.$$

To see whether our requirement for accuracy is satisfied, we must check the values of the polynomial for $x = \pi/8$ and $x = 3\pi/8$.

We find

$$P_3(\pi/8) = (5\sqrt{2} - 1)/16, \; y = \sqrt{2 - \sqrt{2}}/2$$

$$\therefore \quad |y - P_3(\pi/8)| = |0.383 - 0.379| = |0.004| < 0.01$$

and

$$P_3(3\pi/8) = (7\sqrt{2} + 5)/16, \; y = \sqrt{2 + \sqrt{2}}/2$$

$$\therefore \quad |y - P_3(3\pi/8)| = |0.924 - 0.931| = |-0.007| < 0.01.$$

We are well within our tolerance. The results above indicate the following:

$$y \ge P_3(x), \quad 0 \le x \le \pi/4$$
$$y \le P_3(x), \quad \pi/4 \le x \le \pi/2.$$

Figure 18 shows the results.

Exercises

1. (a) Prove: $P_n(-x) = -P_n(x)$ if and only if $P_n(x)$ consists only of odd powers of x.
   (b) Prove: $P_n(-x) = P_n(x)$ if and only if $P_n(x)$ consists only of even powers of x.
2. How does the number of conditions placed upon $P_n(x)$ depend upon n if $P_n(x)$ consists only of odd powers of x, such as in the problem of this section?

3. Let
$$y = \sin x \approx P_2(x), \qquad 0 \leq x \leq \pi/2,$$
exact for $x = 0$, $\pi/4$, $\pi/2$, and find $P_2(x)$. Compare the results with the values of $P_3(x)$ found in this section. Sketch the curves.

4. Use the property that $\cos(-x) = \cos x$ and find $P_n(x)$ as an approximation for $\cos x$, with a tolerance of 0.05 for $-\pi/2 \leq x \leq \pi/2$. Sketch the curves.

5. Find a polynomial approximation for $\cos x$ for $0 \leq x \leq \pi/2$, not using the property of problem 4 but with the same tolerance. Sketch the curves.

6. Can we be sure of the inequalities relating $\sin x$ and $P_n(x)$ as implied by the figures in this section?

7. To what value can the tolerance T be reduced in this section if $\sin x$ is approximated by $P_5(x)$ instead of $P_3(x)$?

4. Method of Lagrange

Although the method of the previous sections is straightforward, it leads to the solution of simultaneous equations with new coefficients for each expression to be approximated and for each set of values to be approximated. Each problem appears to demand a fresh start.

Yet, what is the basic problem as stated? It would seem that it could be resolved into the following problem.

Given the ordered pairs, with distinct first elements, (x_0, y_0), (x_1, y_1), (x_2, y_2), ..., (x_n, y_n) find a polynomial $P_n(x)$ such that the equation
$$y = P_n(x)$$
is satisfied by these $n + 1$ ordered pairs. That is,
$$y_i = P_n(x_i), \qquad i = 0, 1, 2, \ldots, n.$$
Note that we make no requirement that the differences
$$x_1 - x_0, x_2 - x_1, \ldots, x_n - x_{n-1}$$
be equal, only that each one be nonzero.

Now we see that it makes no difference whether the y_i's are computed as the values of specific expressions, such as $x^{1/2}$ or $\sin x$, for given values of x, or whether they are simply data gathered from some experiment, where there is no explicit algebraic or trigonometric relation between x and y.

Let us take an example to motivate the general procedure.

Given the ordered pairs
$$(x_0, y_0), (x_1, y_1), (x_2, y_2)$$
we ask for a polynomial $P_2(x)$ such that
$$y_i = P_2(x_i), \qquad i = 0, 1, 2.$$
Now we know that a quadratic expression can be written as the product of two linear factors. Furthermore, we want each value of y_i to depend

upon x_i and not on some other value of x. This suggests that we could write our $P_2(x)$ as the sum of quadratics, two of which would be zero for a given x_i while the other would give the value of y_i. We try

$$P_2(x) = (x - x_0)(x - x_1)y_2 + (x - x_0)(x - x_2)y_1 + (x - x_1)(x - x_2)y_0.$$

This gives us our sum of three quadratics, two of which are zero for say $x = x_1$, but the other then gives the value

$$(x_1 - x_0)(x_1 - x_2)y_1$$

instead of just y_1. To correct this it would only be necessary to divide the second quadratic by $(x_1 - x_0)(x_1 - x_2)$, which is a nonzero constant, and we obtain y_1.

Naturally the same problem arises in each case, and we have finally

$$P_2(x) = \frac{(x - x_1)(x - x_2)y_0}{(x_0 - x_1)(x_0 - x_2)} + \frac{(x - x_0)(x - x_2)y_1}{(x_1 - x_0)(x_1 - x_2)} + \frac{(x - x_0)(x - x_1)y_2}{(x_2 - x_0)(x_2 - x_1)}$$

which will give us

$$P_2(x_0) = y_0, \quad P_2(x_1) = y_1, \quad P_2(x_2) = y_2.$$

It is easy now to generalize the formula. But because of the room which it takes to write a general formula, and also because of the symmetry of the terms, we use a new notation.

Definition.

$$\prod_{i=1}^{n} b_i = b_1 b_2 b_3 \cdots b_n,$$

that is, the product of all of the b's from b_1 to b_n, inclusive.

For example,

$$\prod_{i=1}^{5} i = 1 \times 2 \times 3 \times 4 \times 5 = 5!$$

$$\prod_{\substack{i=1 \\ i \neq 2}}^{4} (x_i - 1) = (x_1 - 1)(x_3 - 1)(x_4 - 1).$$

This product symbol is analogous to the summation symbol Σ introduced in Chapter 6.

We write our special case in symbolic form first, and then we will write our general formula.

$$P_2(x) = \sum_{k=0}^{2} y_k \frac{\displaystyle\prod_{\substack{i=0 \\ i \neq k}}^{2} (x - x_i)}{\displaystyle\prod_{\substack{i=0 \\ i \neq k}}^{2} (x_k - x_i)} = \sum_{k=0}^{2} y_k \prod_{\substack{i=0 \\ i \neq k}}^{2} \frac{(x - x_i)}{(x_k - x_i)} .$$

While

$$P_n(x) = \sum_{k=0}^{n} y_k \prod_{\substack{i=0 \\ i \neq k}}^{n} \frac{(x - x_i)}{(x_k - x_i)} .$$

This is known as Lagrange's interpolation formula.

The student should observe that it will not give the same answer as the method we used for the approximation of the sin x. The difficulty there was that we skipped the second degree term.

Since there are so few restrictions on it, this formula is quite useful. But the calculations will still be tedious, and it should be remarked that truncation errors certainly will have to be considered if decimals are used. The best procedure is to leave all conversions to decimals until as near the last as possible. A further difficulty is that this formula does not give the coefficients of each term of the polynomial directly. This may be a great disadvantage in some problems.

Exercises

1. Write out the separate terms for Lagrange's formula when $n = 3$.
2. Calculate the approximation for $y = 1/(1 + x)$ by Lagrange's formula for

$$x_0 = 0, \quad x_1 = \tfrac{1}{4}, \quad x_2 = \tfrac{1}{2} \quad \text{and} \quad x_3 = 1.$$

3. Find an approximate formula for $y = x^{1/3}$, valid for $x = 0$, $x = \tfrac{1}{8}$, $x = 1$ by Lagrange's formula. Compare the result for $x = \tfrac{1}{27}$ with the correct answer. Sketch your estimate of the actual curve and approximation curve.

4. Calculate

$$\prod_{n=1}^{4} n^2, \qquad \prod_{n=0}^{3} (n + 1)^2,$$

$$\prod_{n=1}^{5} \frac{n}{n + 1}, \qquad \prod_{n=1}^{k} \frac{n}{n + 1} .$$

5. Is $\displaystyle\sum_{h=1}^{3} \left(\prod_{i=0}^{3} (i + h) \right) = \prod_{h=1}^{3} \left(\sum_{i=0}^{3} (i + h) \right)$?

6. Find $P_2(x)$ for $x^{1/2}$ by the method of Lagrange for the same points used in Section 2 of this chapter. Then expand the result and collect like terms to compare with the previous result. Which procedure seems to be preferable in this problem?

5. Fortran Programs

An iterative procedure for numerical calculations is ideally suited for use with an electronic computer. Given a recurrence relation, the problem of programming is almost trivial. The case of the method of finding the square root of a number, given in Section 1 is a good illustration.

A flow chart follows.

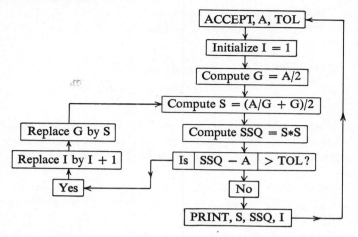

The program calls for the initial guess to always be half the number, and is quite arbitrary. It could be improved upon by including it in the input statement, but the time required to determine a better guess and type in such a number would be far longer than to have the computer start with even a poor guess.

The counter I is included to give the number of iterations necessary for the desired accuracy. TOL is the difference allowed between the number and the square of its computed square root.

The absolute value of SSQ — A is necessary because SSQ may be greater than as well as less than A, depending upon the number.

The Fortran program would be

```
   10 ACCEPT, A, TOL
      I = 1
      G = A/2.
    4 S = (A/G + G)/2.
      SSQ = S*S
      IF (ABS(SSQ − A) − TOL) 2, 2, 3
    3 I = I + 1
      G = S
      GO TO 4
    2 PRINT, S, SSQ, I
      GO TO 10
      END
```

In the case of an iteration method that might go a long while before the result is printed, it would probably be desirable to include some instruction to allow certain values to be printed at the discretion of the operator. This would prevent slowing down the operation by excessive print outs. Here is where the sense switches could be used to advantage, such as

```
3 I = I + 1
  IF(SENSE SWITCH 2) 5, 6,
5 PRINT, S, SSQ, I
6 G = S
```

meaning, if sense switch 2 is on then print, and if the sense switch is off then go directly to statement number 6. Any one, or a combination, of the sense switches may be used to vary the program as the operator deems necessary.

Once we have a polynomial approximation for some expression, such as sin x, we may wish to use it to compute values of the expression, or simply to test it for intermediate values of the independent variable to verify its accuracy for some other use. However, by careful programming the computer may also save a great deal of the algebra involved in determining the original coefficients.

To find the coefficients is essentially a problem in simultaneous equations, but the number of equations in many practical problems may be so few that the Gauss-Jordan method may not be necessary. We illustrate as follows. Consider $P_3(x)$ found in Section 3 of this chapter.

Having found a_3 by elimination as

$$a_3 = 32(1 - \sqrt{2})/3\pi^3,$$

we write

$$a_1 = (2/\pi)(1 - a_3(\pi/2)^3)$$

and let the computer evaluate a_1 for us.

In the following program let us compute the numerical value of each coefficient, evaluate $P_3(x)$ for given steps of values of x and compare the answers with the value of sin x as given by the Fortran subroutine. We shall use A1 and A3 for coefficients, X as the variable, XINC as the amount by which X is to be increased (its increment), XMAX as the maximum value of X, P3X as the value of $P_3(x)$, SX as the value of sin x given by the subroutine, SQ2 as the square root of 2, PI as π, and DIFF as the difference between the values of P3X and SX for a given value of X. The flow chart is shown on page 145.

The reason for printing A1 and A3 at the point indicated is to prevent printing them each time X is changed. Remember that A1 and A3 are constants. We accept both P1 and SQ2 so that we may use any desired accuracy up to the limits of the computer and to prevent using a subroutine to compute SQ2.

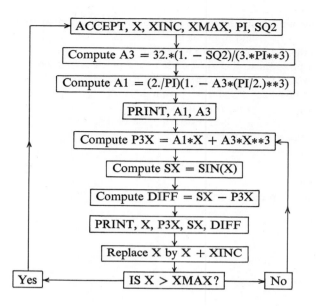

The Fortran program is as follows.

```
1 ACCEPT, X, XINC, XMAX, PI, SQ2
  A3 = 32.*(1. − SQ2)/(3.*PI*PI*PI)
  A1 = (2./PI)(1. − A3*(PI/2.)*(PI/2.)*(PI/2.))
  PRINT, A1, A3
2 P3X = X*(A1 + A3*X*X)
  SX = SIN(X)
  DIFF = SX − P3X
  PRINT, X, P3X, SX, DIFF
  X = X + XINC
  IF(X − XMAX) 2, 2, 1
  END
```

Exercises

1. Write a general recurrence relation from the one given for a square root and the one in problem 4, Section 1, for a cube root, to find the nth root of a number. By using a Fortran program, determine for which value of n the relation does not seem to give the desired root. Include optional print outs as necessary.

2. Use the formula in problem 5, Section 1, to write a program to find the value of π. Use the results of problem 6, Section 1, to do the same.

3. Write a program to determine the area under $y = x^2$, $0 \leq x \leq b$, using the recurrence relation found in problem 1, Section 1. Print out the number of iterations and compare the answer with the exact value for accuracy.

4. (*a*) Write a program to test the accuracy of the polynomial approximation for $y = x^{1/3}$ found in problem 3, Section 2.

(*b*) Do the same for problem 4, Section 2.

5. Write a program to find $\sin x$ and $\cos x$ from second degree polynomials for $0 \leq x \leq \pi/2$ and check the accuracy by using the relation $\sin^2 x + \cos^2 x = 1$. Use results of problems 3 and 5 in Section 3.

6. Write a program comparing the values of $\sin x$ as approximated by $P_3(x)$ and $P_5(x)$ for $0 \leq x \leq \pi/2$. See problem 7, Section 3.

7. Write a program to determine

$$\prod_{n=0}^{k} (n + 1)^2 \text{ and } \prod_{n=1}^{k} \frac{n}{n + 1}.$$

8. Write a program to evaluate Lagrange's interpolation formula for a given value of x.

ANSWERS (SELECTED PROBLEMS)

Chapter 1

SECTION 1

1. (a) Set of all integers. All positive integers. All positive even integers.
   (b) Same as (a).
2. (a) Set of all integers. Set of all odd integers.
   (b) Set of all odd integers. Set of all odd positive integers.
3. Set of all rational numbers contains the set of all odd integers, all even integers and the set consisting of only $\frac{1}{2}$ and $\frac{1}{3}$.
5. $x = 1, y = 1$; $x = -2, y = 3$ in the set of integers.
   $x = 0, y = \frac{5}{3}$; $x = 2, y = \frac{1}{3}$ in the set of rationals.
7. $x^2 - 2x - 3$; $4x^2 - 8x + 3$; $3x^2 - 7x + 2$.

SECTION 2

3. Yes.
4. Yes.
5. Yes.
6. $-a - bi$. $a/(a^2 + b^2) - ib/(a^2 + b^2)$.

SECTION 4

3. No. It is not closed. $2 \times 3 = 0$.
4. No. It is not closed. $1 + 1 = 2$.
6. 1 under multiplication. J_2 under addition.

SECTION 5

1.
J_6	J_7	J_6	J_7
0	1	0	1
1	3	1	5
2	2	2	4
3	6	3	6
4	4	4	2
5	5	5	3

2. Yes.
0	I
1	RTS
2	ROE
3	RN

3. Yes.
1	1
2	$-i$
3	i
4	-1

7. 6.

SECTION 6

2. $P_1^{-1} = P_2;\ P_3^{-1} = P_3;\ P_4^{-1} = P_4;\ P_5^{-1} = P_5;\ P_6^{-1} = P_6.$
3. (a) P_5. (b) P_3.
6. I, (12)(34).
7. (54)(716)(32).
9. No.

Chapter 2

SECTION 1

1. (a) $\begin{pmatrix} 16 & -22 \\ 22 & 38 \end{pmatrix}$ (b) $\begin{pmatrix} 5 & -4 \\ -1 & 7 \end{pmatrix}$ (c) $\begin{pmatrix} -2 \\ 77 \end{pmatrix}$

3. $\begin{pmatrix} 16 & 1 \\ 3 & 10 \end{pmatrix}$

4. $\begin{pmatrix} -1 & 8 \\ 21 & 11 \\ 0 & -5 \end{pmatrix}$

6. $a = 2.\ b = 1.$
8. Number of rows are equal. Number of columns are equal.

9. $\begin{pmatrix} 1 & 7 \\ 7 & 3 \end{pmatrix};\ \begin{pmatrix} 7 & 2 \\ 11 & 6 \end{pmatrix};\ \begin{pmatrix} 1 & 7 \\ 7 & 3 \end{pmatrix};\ \begin{pmatrix} 14 & 17 \\ -2 & -1 \end{pmatrix}.$

SECTION 2

2. $AB = \begin{pmatrix} 24 & 11 \\ 10 & 10 \end{pmatrix}$; $BA = \begin{pmatrix} 10 & 22 \\ 5 & 24 \end{pmatrix}$.

3. $AB = BA = \begin{pmatrix} 4 & -1 \\ 2 & 4 \end{pmatrix}$.

5. No. $C = \begin{pmatrix} 2 \\ 3 \end{pmatrix}$

6. (a) $IA = A$. $IB = B$.

9. (a) $2I = (a_{ij})$, $a_{ij} = 2$, $i = j$
$\qquad\qquad\qquad a_{ij} = 0$, $i \neq j$
   (b) $2IA = (b_{ij})$
      where $b_{ij} = 2a_{ij}$ for all i, j.
   (c) $(-1)IA = (b_{ij})$
      where $b_{ij} = -a_{ij}$ for all i, j.

SECTION 3

1. $A^{-1} = \begin{pmatrix} -3/6 & -3/6 \\ 4/6 & 2/6 \end{pmatrix}$

2. Rank is 1 which is less than the order.

3. (a) Yes. $(-1) = (-1)(1) + 0(i)$.
   (b) No. $1(i) + 1(-i) = 0$.
   (c) Yes. $0(i) + 0(-1) = 0$ is only possible linear combination.
   (d) Yes. $-i = 1(1) + 1(-1) + 1(i) + 2(-i)$.

5. 2.

6. Rank is 3 which equals the order.

$$\begin{pmatrix} 14/364 & 56/364 & 70/364 \\ -133/364 & 14/364 & 63/364 \\ -63/364 & -70/364 & 49/364 \end{pmatrix}$$

7. 1.

SECTION 4

3. $B = \begin{pmatrix} 1/14 & -3/14 \\ 2/7 & 1/7 \end{pmatrix}$, $BA = I$

4. (a) $x = \dfrac{125}{130}$, $y = \dfrac{-35}{130}$

(b) $x = \dfrac{120}{130}$, $y = \dfrac{-70}{130}$

Only if the constants are equal.

6. (a) No. (b) No.

1. (a) $x_1 = 29/7$, $x_2 = -3/7$.
   (b) $x_1 = 1$, $x_2 = 2$, $x_3 = 3$.
   (c) $x_1 = 1$, $x_2 = -1$, $x_3 = 4$.

2. (a) $\begin{pmatrix} 4/14 & 6/14 \\ 2/14 & -4/14 \end{pmatrix}$

   (b) $\begin{pmatrix} 5/26 & 3/26 & -1/26 \\ 2/26 & -4/26 & 10/26 \\ -9/26 & 5/26 & 7/26 \end{pmatrix}$

   (c) $\begin{pmatrix} -1/8 & -1/8 & 3/8 \\ 3/8 & 3/8 & -1/8 \\ 2/8 & -6/8 & 2/8 \end{pmatrix}$

3. $x_1 = 1$, $x_2 = -2$, $x_3 = 2$, $x_4 = 4$.

   $\begin{pmatrix} 67/141 & 45/141 & -14/141 & 12/141 \\ -25/141 & -21/141 & 41/141 & -15/141 \\ 5/141 & -24/141 & 20/141 & 3/141 \\ -39/141 & 18/141 & -15/141 & 33/141 \end{pmatrix}$

5. $x_1 = \frac{3}{2}$, $x_2 = \frac{1}{2} - x_3$.

6. $b \neq -2$ gives unique solutions.
   $b = -2$, $(1, -3, -2) = 1(1, 2, 3) - 2(3, 1, 4)$.

Chapter 4

4. J_6 under addition and multiplication.
   $2 \times 4 = 2 \times 1$, but $4 \neq 1$.

2. Even integers under addition and multiplication.

4. Yes. Yes.

SECTION 3

1. $x = 2$.
2. $x = 3$.
3. $x = 3$.
4. $2x + 1 = 4$ in ring of integers.
   $2x + 1 = 4$ in J_5.
   $2x + 1 = 5$ in J_6.

SECTION 4

4. Yes.
5. Yes.

SECTION 5

1. $x = 4$.
2. $x = 1$. No.
4. No. Yes.

SECTION 6

3. No. $\sqrt{2}$ has no inverse.
4. Yes.
5. $(-0) = 0, (-1) = 6, (-2) = 5, (-3) = 4, (-4) = 3, (-5) = 2, (-6) = 1$.
   $1^{-1} = 1, 2^{-1} = 4, 3^{-1} = 5, 4^{-1} = 2, 5^{-1} = 3, 6^{-1} = 6$.
6. No to all parts.

SECTION 7

2. $x = 1$. $x = 1$.
5. $ix = 1$.
6. $x = -2$. $x = -2$. $x = 5$. No.

Chapter 5

SECTION 1

1. $x_1 = 0.33, x_2 = 2.0$.
2. 1950. 1950. 1950.
   1640. 1640. 1650.
3. 82000. 79000. 83000.
   13000. 13000. 13000.
4. (a) If $A + B$ is divisible by 10.
      If $A + B$ is divisible by 100.

(b) If $A + B$ is divisible by 100, and A and B are both divisible by 50.
If the sums of corresponding digits are all less than 10.
If $A + B$ is divisible by 100.
If $A + B$ is less than 1001 and divisible by 10.
(c) If AB is divisible by 100.
If AB is less than 1001 and divisible by 10.
$T(A) = A$. $T(B) = B$. See previous answers.

SECTION 2

2. Solutions belong to set of integers after truncation. Irrational before.
3. No solutions after truncation. Unique solution before.
4. $x^2 + 6x + 4$.

SECTION 3

6. Condition (c). Similar triangles.

SECTION 4

1. (a) $-2 < x < 2$
   (b) $-2 < x < 2$
   $-\infty < y < \infty$
2. (a) $\qquad\qquad x < 1$
   $2x/3 + 4/3 < y < -3x/4 + 11/4$
   (b) $\qquad\qquad x > 1$
   $-3x/4 + 11/4 < y < 2x/3 + 4/3$
   (c) $\qquad\qquad y > 2$
   $-4y/3 + 11/3 < x < 3y/2 - 2$
3. $-3 \leq x < 4$.
   $x^2 < 0$.
   $x^2 \leq 0$.
   $x^2 > 0$.
4. $x^2 + y^2 > 1, x < 2, x > -2, y < 2, y > -2$.
   $x^2 + y^2 > 1, x + y < 2\sqrt{2}, x + y > -2\sqrt{2}, x - y < 2\sqrt{2}$,
   $x - y > -2\sqrt{2}$.
6. $x > 2$ or $x < 0$.
   $0 < x < 2$.
7. $1 - \sqrt{2} < x < 1 + \sqrt{2}$.
   $x < 1 - \sqrt{2}$ or $x > 1 + \sqrt{2}$.

SECTION 5

2. (a) 1.
   (b) Up to 0.0261 (or 1°30′) to the closest ten minutes and truncated.
5. Varies with θ.

Chapter 6

SECTION 1

1. $A = b^4/4$.
2. $A = b^5/5$.
3. $n = 96$. $1/18432$ of A more than $1/64$ of A.
4. $n = 12$. Difference for successive values of n does not give true value of accuracy.
5. Not closer.

SECTION 3

3. $r = 17/15$. n is the first integer greater than $\dfrac{\log\ b/a}{\log 17/15}$.

6. 64.
7. $\frac{2}{3}$.
8. (a) $4\frac{1}{2}$. (b) Yes. Curve lies below the x axis in part.

SECTION 4

4. Within 0.2 truncated.
5. $A = \sin b$.
6. Answers are the same if the interval is moved $\pi/2$ units.
7. 2 units of area under any arch.

Chapter 7

SECTION 1

1. $2(n + 1)^2 A_{n+1} = 2n^2 A_n + b^3/3[4n + 5]$
2. $4A_{2n} = 2A_n + b^2$
4. Yes.
5. $A_n = n/2 \sin 2\pi/n$

SECTION 2

1. $P_4(x) = (77 - 6\sqrt{2} - 16\sqrt{3})x/15 + (-214 - 18\sqrt{2} + 112\sqrt{3})x^2/15$
   $+ (88 + 216\sqrt{2} - 224\sqrt{3})x^3/15 + (64 - 192\sqrt{2} + 128\sqrt{3})x^4/15$
2. Double the degree.
3. $P_2(x) = (-1 + 2\sqrt[3]{4})x + (2 - 2\sqrt[3]{4})x^2$
5. $P_2(x) = \dfrac{10 - 3x - 2x^2}{10}$

   approximate area $= 0.7833$
   exact area $= 0.7853$

2. $\dfrac{n+1}{2}$

3. $P_2(x) = (-2 + 4\sqrt{2})x/\pi + (8 - 8\sqrt{2})x^2/\pi^2$

$P_2(\pi/8) = 0.405$ Less accurate than $P_3(\pi/8)$.

$P_2(3\pi/8) = 0.905$ Less accurate than $P_3(3\pi/8)$.

4. $P_2(x) = 1 - \dfrac{4x^2}{\pi^2}$

$P_2(\pi/4) = 0.750$, $\cos \pi/4 = 0.707$

$|0.750 - 0.707| = 0.043 < 0.05$

6. Not without further information.

SECTION 4

2. $y_0 = 1$, $y_1 = \frac{4}{5}$, $y_2 = \frac{2}{3}$, $y_3 = \frac{1}{2}$.

$$P_3(x) = \frac{(x - \frac{1}{4})(x - \frac{1}{2})(x - 1)}{(0 - \frac{1}{4})(0 - \frac{1}{2})(0 - 1)}(1) + \frac{(x - 0)(x - \frac{1}{2})(x - 1)}{(\frac{1}{4} - 0)(\frac{1}{4} - \frac{1}{2})(\frac{1}{4} - 1)}(\tfrac{4}{5})$$
$$+ \frac{(x - 0)(x - \frac{1}{4})(x - 1)}{(\frac{1}{2} - 0)(\frac{1}{2} - \frac{1}{4})(\frac{1}{2} - 1)}(\tfrac{2}{3}) + \frac{(x - 0)(x - \frac{1}{4})(x - \frac{1}{2})}{(1 - 0)(1 - \frac{1}{4})(1 - \frac{1}{2})}(\tfrac{1}{2}).$$

3. $y_0 = 0$, $y_1 = \frac{1}{2}$, $y_2 = 1$

$$P_2(x) = \frac{(x - \frac{1}{8})(x - 1)}{(0 - \frac{1}{8})(0 - 1)}(0) + \frac{(x - 0)(x - 1)}{(\frac{1}{8} - 0)(\frac{1}{8} - 1)}(\tfrac{1}{2})$$
$$+ \frac{(x - 0)(x - \frac{1}{8})}{(1 - 0)(1 - \frac{1}{8})}(1).$$

$P_2(1/27) = 0.159$. $\sqrt[3]{1/27} = 0.333$.

4. 576; 576; $\frac{1}{6}$; $1/k + 1$.

5. No.

INDEX